**Services and Maintenance
for Hotels and
Residential Establishments**

Uniform with this volume

Housekeeping Management for
Hotels and Residential Establishments

by Rosemary Hurst

Services and Maintenance For Hotels and Residential Establishments

Rosemary Hurst

HEINEMANN : LONDON

William Heinemann Ltd
10 Upper Grosvenor Street, London W1X 9PA

LONDON   MELBOURNE   TORONTO
JOHANNESBURG   AUCKLAND

0 434 90793 6

Printed in Great Britain by
Biddles Ltd, Guildford, Surrey

INTRODUCTION

The Hotel and Catering Industry is very varied with its members operating and managing in hotels, schools, colleges, and universities, as well as providing a wide range of welfare and supporting services. Within the industry, good maintenance plays an essential part in upholding the standards of comfortable and attractive premises and accommodation.

In a great number of smaller hotels and establishments, the responsibility for housekeeping and maintenance is frequently undertaken by the wife of the manager or proprietor or by a competent assistant who often has had no formal training. It is hoped that they will find the following chapters of use when they come to consider the many problems that can arise. Poor maintenance can be extremely costly.

Services and Maintenance has been planned, with its companion volume *Housekeeping Management for Hotels and Residential Establishments*, to meet the requirements of the syllabus for the examining body of the Hotel Catering and Institutional Management Association. It is also intended to provide a framework for all students entering the industry whether they wish to work in hotels, clubs or other residential establishments.

In both books, I have tried to explain the principles and ideas behind all planning and control.

ACKNOWLEDGMENTS

Without advice and encouragement from many friends this book would not have been completed; to them I am very grateful.

I wish to thank particularly the many firms who have given assistance and also the following who have given permission for the reproduction of some of the diagrams and illustrations which I have needed:

The Air Conditioning Advisory Bureau	(4.3, 4.4, 4.5)
The Architects' Journal	(1.6)
Matthew Hall (Mechanical Services) Ltd.	(5.13)

and with permission from the Controller of Her Majesty's Stationery Office illustrations from:

I must also thank the three motoring organizations, the Royal Automobile Club, the Automobile Association, and the Royal Scottish Automobile Club for permission to include notes on their Classification of Requirements for Accommodation Services in hotels.

R.H.

CONTENTS

1 LAYOUT AND ACCOMMODATION

GENERAL PRINCIPLES

IT is no part of the design of this book to teach the reader how to become an architect, maintenance or heating engineer; the intention is that the reader should be able to appreciate the basic principles and ideas which are involved when new buildings are being planned and when old buildings are renovated or adapted for different purposes.

When a building is planned, consideration is given to:

1. The main activities and needs of the users.
2. The numbers likely to be in any particular area at any one time – the use density.
3. The main traffic lanes in the building and the amount of circulation area which will be needed to give easy access to all rooms.
4. The space requirements within each room to allow for the comfortable use of furniture and equipment.
5. The standard of accommodation and service which is to be offered and, especially in the case of hotels, the category of customer it is wished to attract.
6. The space needed to service and maintain the building; provision must be made for stock-rooms, linen-rooms, cleaner's cupboards, and staff accommodation.

And, what is essential, the safety factors and regulations which govern the use of the building.

In the International Labour Office's *Review of Social and Economic Problems of Employees in Hotels* it is stressed that 'safety is inseparably bound up with work organization and, consequently, special thought should be given to the prevention of occupational accidents when designing the buildings and when purchasing and installing machinery'. Safety, which includes both fire and accident prevention, must always be considered. The Health and Safety at Work Act, 1974 makes it a duty for both employers and employees to take all reasonable precautions to ensure the safety and welfare of both staff and guests and all other people who have access to the premises.

THE MAIN ACTIVITIES AND NEEDS
OF THE USER

Most hotels and residential establishments provide accommodation
for their guests who fall into one or more of the following groups.

Group	Length of stay	Type of user	Type of establishment
A	1 or 2 nights	Businessmen Overnight travellers	Hotels
B	1 or 2 weeks	Long-term business-men Holidaymakers Conferences	Hotels University and college residences during vacations
C	Short-term residence 3 to 30 weeks	Students Resident guests	Hotels University and college residences
D	Long-term or per-manent	Resident staff – hospital, college, etc. Retired people	Hospital residences Hotels Old people's homes and residences

Each group has the same basic need – to be made to feel welcome
and to be treated cheerfully and courteously by the staff. Each will
want comfortable warm accommodation, with the beds and furnishings clean, attractive, and well maintained. Not all groups will want
or need be supplied with the same facilities for storage, laundry, and
entertainment.

Group A

This group requires space in which reports, orders, or business letters
can be written; so a table which can be used as a desk with a chair
of the right height should be provided. In addition to the telephone
the guest may also need a plug to which a dictaphone can be connected or he may expect the hotel to provide the occasional use of a
short-hand typist. When needed, the room should be suitable to
entertain business acquaintances to whom he should be able to offer
drinks, coffee, and sandwiches. Often a stranger to the district, a
sketch-map showing the lay-out of the town with the focal points of
interest and entertainments will be useful.

Cupboard and drawer space can be reduced to a minimum but
normally drip-dry facilities are required for socks and shirts even if
this is only in the form of a rail or hanger over the bath.

Group B

This group requires more storage space as suitcases are usually completely unpacked, with space also allowed for empty cases to be put

out of the way. Some laundry or washing and ironing facilities may be needed beyond that of drip-drying above the bath or hand-basin.

If the hotel is in a holiday resort, extra lounge and recreational rooms may be needed for periods when the weather is bad; and facilities for baby-sitting may be required. Where the hotel is also run for small conferences, rooms must be available which can be blacked out for film or slide projection; these rooms must be quiet to enable guests to write and talk undisturbed. Smaller rooms may also be necessary for discussion groups or seminars.

Group C

Basically, their needs will be as for group B but they will have a greater demand for a utility room where washing, drying, and ironing can be done and where tea, coffee, and snacks can be prepared. Bed-sittingrooms may need to be larger to allow for entertaining; and there is need for a greater variety of public rooms to accommodate hobbies, craft and practice rooms, indoor games, and group meetings.

Group D

Planning for this group can be difficult as, to them, the hotel or residence is often their permanent home and, whilst it is difficult to meet every demand, the management should be as flexible as possible. It is to be expected that permanent or semi-permanent residents will bring with them many of their own possessions and will use their own covers, cushions, pictures, and small items of furniture. Often only basic furniture is provided, which means that room-maids have a more varied and difficult task with great care being needed with the individual possessions.

Extra storage space must be provided to take trunks and suit-cases.

Where an hotel or college residence is isolated from a town or from the parent buildings, extra common-room or library space must be allocated as more guests or students will remain in the buildings during week-ends and in the evenings than would normally be expected.

Another question an architect has to ask is whether men and women need the same facilities, although it is becoming generally accepted that, apart from such needs as razor points and the preference for shower baths that men seem to have, both have very similar requirements; both need to wash and dry small items of clothing, both like to entertain and make hot drinks and snacks in the evening.

THE NUMBERS LIKELY TO BE IN A PARTICULAR AREA AT ANY ONE TIME AND THE CIRCULATION AREA REQUIRED

This must take into account the activities of the users. An hotel catering mainly for businessmen may have to welcome and book in the greatest proportion of their guests between 5.30 and 7.00 p.m. whilst a country hotel may receive their guests at a steady rate throughout the day. One hotel will need a relatively larger entrance and reception area than the other so that the peak periods can be dealt with smoothly. In the same way, if breakfast is served in a college hostel on the stroke of 8.00 a.m. there may be upwards of 150 students waiting for the doors to open, whereas an hotel which serves continuously from 7.30 a.m. until 10.00 a.m. will not need the same amount of access hall or corridor.

When planning, the relevant fire regulations are important and the local authorities must be consulted. The requirements which the G.L.C. set out in the L.C.C. Code of Practice '*Means of escape in case of fire*' give a useful guide to corridor and staircase widths and the maximum distances which should be covered until a point of safety is reached.

As a guide, the following are some of the minimum areas which are recommended by the *Architects' Journal*. All are based on the size of the average person and the average speed of movement.

For general design purposes, the flow capacities for corridors and staircases is based on 0.8 m^2 (9 ft^2) per person but where people are walking at a good pace as, perhaps, in a connecting corridor, this may be increased to 3.7 m^2 (40 ft^2).

A corridor wide enough to allow two people to pass easily is 1 200 to 1 400 mm (47 to 55 in.) wide; but if the traffic flow is calculated as being more than this, then an extra 750 mm (29 in.) should be allowed for each extra person width.

The minimum widths for escape corridors and stairways in a two-staircase building recommended by the G.L.C. are less than this. For up to 200 people who are evenly distributed on all floors, they recommend 914 mm (36 in.) and, for up to 300 people, 1 066 mm (42 in.).

The minimum area needed for people seated closely together in an assembly hall based on movable seats, usually armless, is 0.46 m^2 (5 ft^2) but, when the seating is fixed, this increases to 0.6 m^2 (6$\frac{1}{2}$ ft^2).

In a restaurant or dining-area, the space allowance is 0.9 to 1.1 m^2 (10 to 12 ft^2) and in a dance hall 0.55 to 0.9 m^2 (6 to 10 ft^2). These figures allow for clearing aisles and passing spaces; but where the room is irregularly shaped or where there are a number of supporting pillars or serveries more space would be needed.

A good overall allowance for waiting areas where everyone is

standing and where there is no cross traffic flow is 0·5 to 0·65 m²
(5 to 7 ft²) but, where provision is made for half the number to sit,
this allowance increases to 1·1 to 1·4 m² (12 to 15 ft²). The greatest
density possible for each square metre (11 ft²) is six people.

Having said all this, architects usually work to an overall gross
area allocation. For example, when designing a residence for college
students the architect may be restricted to the total area of 18·58 m²
(200 ft²) for each student – this to include the study-bedroom, service
rooms, and all circulation and ancillary areas such as bathrooms,
sanitary facilities, and storage space. To gain the maximum amount
of study and living space he will plan to reduce the amount of circulation as much as he can; this has a great effect on the shape and
grouping of the rooms.

When the building design is based on long corridors with rooms
opening from each side, as in Figure 1.1, the space for study-

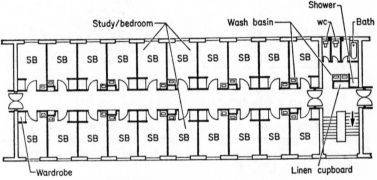

FIGURE 1.1   Central corridor access
The usual monotony of a long corridor has been reduced here by
having corridors of 1·5 m (5 ft) width. The laying of a carpet in
the circulation areas has reduced disturbance in the building from
people walking about. (From *Student Residence*, Building
Bulletin No. 37, Department of Education and Science, 1967).

bedrooms may only be 50·0%, with service rooms 8·9%, circulation
and ancillary rooms 41·1%, making a total of 100·0%.

When rooms are grouped around a central landing the circulation
area is reduced (*see* Figure 1.2). In this case, the percentages might
be as follows:

study-bedroom	63·6%
service rooms	3·1%
circulation and ancillary rooms	33·3%
	100·0%

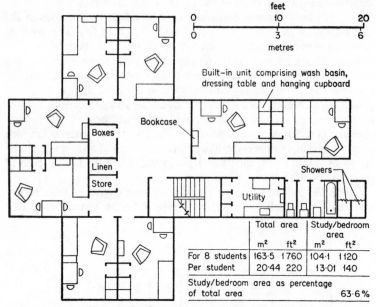

FIGURE 1.2   Access through a central landing
(From *Training College Hostels*, Building Bulletin No. 15,
Ministry of Education, 1957.)

If, however, instead of using a corridor people pass directly into
and use a sittingroom or utility room as a means of access to study-
bedrooms, the circulation area may be further reduced to as little as
16% (*see* Figure 1.3).

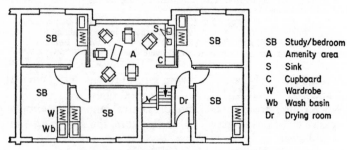

FIGURE 1.3   Access through an amenity area
This design has the domestic quality of two-storey housing. The
amenity area serves ten students and, although circulation passes
through it, all the room doors are kept away from the sitting area.
Note the drying room with access to the small balcony: the
utility room is with the sanitary accommodation on the ground
floor. (From *Student Residence*, Building Bulletin No. 37, Department of Education and Science, 1967.)

As a further example, rooms 3·962 × 2·743 m (13 × 9 ft) which are planned with the longest side at right angles to the corridor have a usable area of 14·40 m² (155 ft²), i.e. 10·87 m² (117 ft²) in the study-bedroom and 3·53 m² (38 ft²) for ancillary and amenity areas. The gross allowance would be 20·16 m² (217 ft²) of which 40% is circulation area in the corridor.

If the same sized rooms are planned with the longest side parallel to the corridor the usable area is still 14·40 m² but the gross area increases to 21·18 m² (228 ft²) of which 48% is circulation area and, of course, there is also a corresponding increase in construction costs.

There are many different possible accommodation arrangements for any type of hostel or hotel.

SPACE REQUIREMENTS WITHIN THE ROOM

The space needed is calculated by adding together the area which each piece of furniture occupies, the amount of space needed to use it, and the space needed for access. Naturally enough, the same access and 'use' space can be utilized for different activities when these do not conflict.

As an example of this, the space which is needed to make a bed is from 355 to 400 mm (14 to 16 in.) at each side and 200 to 250 mm (8 to 10 in.) at the end, but for ease of movement around the beds more space is required (*see* Figure 1.4). To take clothes from a chest of drawers 700 to 1000 mm (27 to 39 in.) are required (*see* Figure 1.5). Other examples are shown in Figures 1.6 to 1.10.

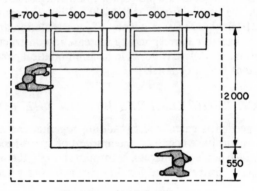

Circulation around twin beds

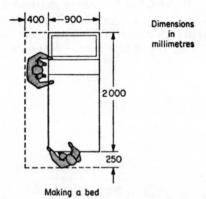

Dimensions
in
millimetres

Making a bed

FIGURE 1.4   Space requirements for circulation around
(From *Space in the Home* (metric edition), Design Bulletin No. 6,
Ministry of Housing and Local Government, reprinted 1970.)

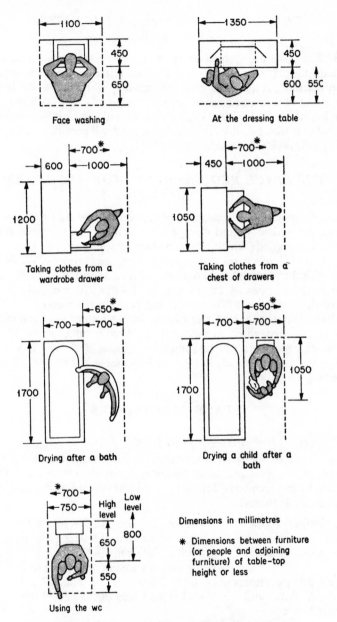

Face washing

At the dressing table

Taking clothes from a wardrobe drawer

Taking clothes from a chest of drawers

Drying after a bath

Drying a child after a bath

Using the wc

Dimensions in millimetres

* Dimensions between furniture (or people and adjoining furniture) of table-top height or less

FIGURE 1.5 Space requirements for various activities (From *Space in the Home* (metric edition), Design Bulletin No. 6, Ministry of Housing and Local Government, reprinted 1970.)

THE STANDARD OF ACCOMMODATION AND SERVICE

Building costs are quoted as so many £s to the square metre or square foot so that minimum standards relate to the basic cost of constructing, furnishing, and maintaining a bedroom or study-bedroom of an agreed minimum size. Standards vary with the size, quality of finish, facilities, and services offered, which it is considered will attract the desired level of customer, and will provide an adequate return on capital invested.

THE SPACE REQUIREMENTS FOR ANCILLARY ROOMS

These include stock rooms, storage cupboards, and staff cloakrooms. Areas for bulk stock and storage depend entirely on the amount and sizes of the goods which are to be kept. As an example, one single sheet, folded to go on a linenroom shelf, measures 610 × 230 mm (24 × 9 in.) and has a height of about 30 mm (1¼ in.). When 100 sheets are stored in piles of 25, an area of 2 440 × 920 mm (96 × 36 in.) is needed with about 800 mm (31 in.) between the shelves.

In the same way, staff rest rooms, locker rooms and cloakrooms are equally dependent on the numbers. What is sufficient for 20 full-time staff members will be totally inadequate if 40 part-timers are employed in their stead; but it may be suitable if the hours of work are staggered.

SPACE ALLOWANCES

HOTELS

The standards for space allowances for hotel accommodation vary considerably from one hotel to another but the information sheet issued by the Architects' Journal in 1965 gives the following minimum recommended sizes:

For a single room	3 800 × 2 600 mm (12 ft 6 in. × 8 ft 6 in.) giving an area of 9·9 m² (106 ft²)
For a double room	4 400 × 3 800 mm (14 ft 6 in. × 12 ft 6 in.) giving an area of 16·7 m² (178 ft²)
For a private bathroom (bath, W.C., and handbasin)	1 600 × 2 200 mm (5 ft 3 in. × 7 ft 3 in.) giving an area of 3·5 m² (38 ft²)

Where private baths are fitted, space can be saved by fitting them on an internal corridor and not on an external wall (*see* Figure 1.6).

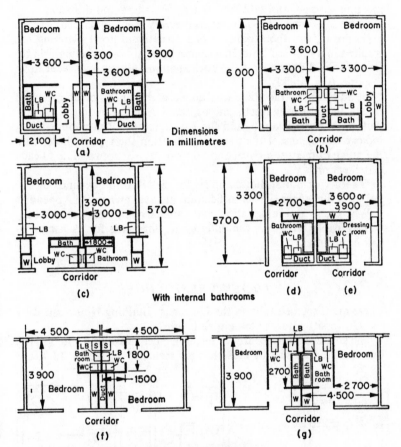

Dimensions in millimetres

With internal bathrooms

W = wardrobe   LB = lavatory (hand) basin   S = shower

With external bathrooms

FIGURE 1.6   Some typical plan arrangements of hotel
bedrooms and bathrooms

Bathrooms
A saving of space is achieved by the use of internal bathrooms.
These require mechanical extract ventilation which can be
easily planned in the service ducts. Sufficient intake ventilation
should be provided by means of a grille or a space under the door.
Flushing cisterns are best accommodated in the service ducts to
prevent tampering as well as to save space.

Lobbies
The lobby can be used as a dressing annexe to the bedroom. With
such an arrangement no door is required between the two spaces
(see *e*). (From *AJ Metric Handbook*.)

Basically, each room provides for the guest, a bed or divan, hanging storage, and table-top space for writing and dressing.

Space lay-outs and requirements are very much individual to each hotel group, but the expansion of international hotel planning has resulted in a modern hotel in Teheran being almost indistinguishable from one in London or New York; national differences seem to be disappearing quickly.

In addition to the standards aimed at by an hotel or group of hotels, the motoring organizations, the Royal Automobile Club, the Automobile Association, and the Royal Scottish Automobile Club, indicate by means of their star classification the type of hotel with the range of menus, service, and hours of service appropriate to each classification.

Whether or not an hotel applies for classification depends on the policy of the owner. The classifications are as shown in the Appendix.

Where the accommodation and housekeeping services are concerned Table 1.1 shows the differing requirements for each classification of hotel.

STUDENT RESIDENCES

These are discussed fully in the University Building Notes issued by the University Grants Committee in 1967.

The smallest study-bedroom recommended is about $6 \cdot 5$ m² (70 ft²) but the average size in most hostels seems to be about $13 \cdot 01$ m²

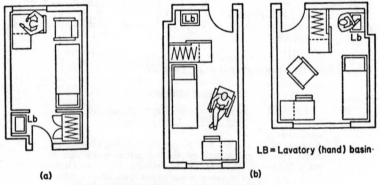

(a)   (b)

FIGURE 1.7   Lay-outs for study-bedrooms
(a) Single study bedroom of $10 \cdot 13$ m² (109 ft²).
(b) Single study bedroom of $11 \cdot 15$ m² (120 ft²).
As well as being cheaper to build, the long narrow room tends to provide a more economical use of space and a clearer division of function. (From *Student Residence*, Building Bulletin No. 37, Department of Education and Science, 1967.)

(140 ft²). This has gradually increased since the early 1950s when the average size was 10·68 m² (115 ft²) and in the late 1950s when it was 12·08 m² (130 ft²). Some layouts are given in Figure 1.7.

Recommendations for ancillary rooms are for one utility room to every ten students with an area of 9·29 m² (100 ft²) or 0·93 m² for each student. This allows for a sink unit and drainer, a crockery store, a food store, a worktop, electric points for an iron or toaster, kettle or small grill, and some seating and perhaps a table.

For baggage, a separate store is suggested on the scale of 0·45 m³ (16 ft³) for each student. There may be a central launderette as one of the communal facilities but, even so, there should be some provision for drip-drying and ironing for each grouping of students. The suggestion is also made that the ironing-board should be fixed so that it cannot be taken to a student's room and that the iron should operate on a time-switch so that the risk of fire is minimized.

In addition to the *bulk stores* needed for cleaning equipment and linen, it is recognized that localized storage is also necessary and that lockable cleaners' cupboards with a low-level sink should be provided particularly if students are to be given any responsibilities for keeping their own quarters clean.

Communal and recreational areas are provided for larger groups when the residence is isolated from the main university or college and it is considered that a reasonable scale for this is at the rate of 0·65 m² (7 ft²) per student. Whether this space is best used as one large communal room or divided into various smaller common-rooms for television, committee meetings, or library and quiet rooms, depends very much on the views of the architect and of the planning committee.

A well-stocked *medicine cupboard* and *first-aid box* should be kept centrally, possibly in the Domestic Bursar's or Housekeeper's office. The Grants Committee feels, however, that as few staff are qualified to cope with more than first-aid or light home nursing, any long-term illness or complication, which would not normally be dealt with at home, should be nursed in hospital. They feel therefore that the provision of clinically equipped sick quarters should be avoided unless they can be used for a dual purpose, such as for *guest-rooms*, and that ordinary domestic care and the provision of meals in a student's room for a few days is all that should be required. In the event of a 'flu epidemic or similar outbreak any small sick quarters would be totally inadequate.

RESIDENTIAL ACCOMMODATION FOR HOSPITAL STAFFS

The Ministry of Health sets out in the Hospital Building Note No. 24, 1964, their recommendations for accommodation. It is considered

	★	★★	★★★
1. BEDROOMS **(a) GENERAL** See also common requirements item Q	Each room to be suitably decorated and furnished and of sufficient size to allow freedom of movement of guests occupying the room	Each room to be suitably decorated and furnished and of sufficient size to allow freedom of movement of guests occupying the room. Luggage stand or equivalent	Furnishings of a generally higher standard. Full length mirror. Wardrobe enclosed by curtain or door
(b) LIGHTING	Adequate lighting with a means of controlling a light from each bed	A reading light for each person or for each double bed with switch accessible to each occupant	A reading light for eac person or for each double bed with switch accessible to each occupant
(c) HEATING (during stay)	Adequate heating at no extra charge	Adequate heating at no extra charge	On/off controlled heating at no extra charge
(d) TELEPHONE/ **INTERNAL** **COMMUNICATION**	Not required	Not required	Means of calling for service during daytime and evening
(e) EARLY MORNING **TEA/COFFEE** *Note*: Only fresh or UHT milk accepted.	Service or provision of full range of equipment including teapot and sufficient materials safely and conveniently situated	Service or provision of full range of equipment including teapot and sufficient materials safely and conveniently situated	Service or provision of full range of equipmen including teapot and sufficient materials safely and conveniently situated
(f) BREAKFAST ROOM **SERVICE**	None except in case of illness	None except in case of illness	Continental breakfast
(g) LUNCH, DINNER & **REFRESHMENTS:** **ROOM SERVICE**	None except in case of illness	None except in case of illness	None except in case of illness
2. SHOE CLEANING	Availability of service, free machine, or provision of materials	Availability of service, free machine, or provision of materials	Availability of service or free machine
3. LAUNDRY, ETC	Not required	Not required	Not required

★★★	★★★★★	☆☆	☆☆☆	☆☆☆☆
comfortable ns	Spacious, luxuriously appointed rooms. Wardrobe enclosed by door	Modern, well furnished rooms with luggage stand or equivalent	Modern rooms with furnishings and equipment of a high standard	Very comfortable and spacious rooms with a superior standard of furnishings and equipment. Open hanging space if situated in entrance lobby or wardrobe enclosed by door or curtain
ading light for person or for double bed switch sible to each pant	A reading light for, and controllable by, each person	A reading light for each person or for each double bed with control accessible to each occupant	A reading light for each person or for each double bed with control accessible to each occupant	A reading light for each person with control accessible to each occupant
ff controlled ng: lementary ng on st at no charge	Adjustable heating; supplementary heating on request at no extra charge	On/off controlled heating; supplementary heating on request at no extra charge	On/off controlled heating; supplementary heating on request at no extra charge	On/off controlled heating; supplementary heating on request at no extra charge
Office hone ating day and t	Post Office Telephone operating day and night	PO telephone daytime and evening. Intercom or bell at all hours	PO relephone daytime and evening. Intercom at all hours	PO telephone operating day and night
ice	Service	Service or provision of full range of equipment including teapot and sufficient materials, safely and conveniently situated	Service or provision of full range of equipment including teapot and sufficient materials, safely and conveniently situated	Service or provision of full range of equipment including teapot and sufficient materials, safely and conveniently situated
ked set kfast	A la carte breakfast service	None except in case of illness	None except in case of illness	Continental Breakfast on request
dishes during ours of lunch dinner. Drinks light shments 24 s per day	Full floor service of meals at all reasonable hours. Drinks and hot light refreshments 24 hours per day	None except in case of illness	None except in case of illness	None except in case of illness
ability of ce	Availability of service	Availability of service or machine	Availability of service or free machine	Availability of service or free machine
our service, ends excepted. lities for ing clothes	24-hour service, weekends excepted. Valet service	Not required	48 hour service weekends excepted	48 hour service weekends excepted. Facilities for pressing clothes

	★	★★	★★★
4. PRIVATE BATH/ SHOWER ROOMS WITH SOME FORM OF HEATING AND WITH LAVATORY EN SUITE *Note:* Satisfactory annexe accommodation may count towards the required ratios.	Not required	A bath or shower in 20% of the bedrooms	2/3's of all bedro provide private facilities. A maxin of 1/ 3 of all bedr may provide show lieu of baths i.e. i bedroom hotel 66 must provide priv facilities which in bedrooms may ta form of shower ar rather than bath a WC
5. GENERAL LAVATORIES SERVING BEDROOMS WITHOUT PRIVATE FACILITIES	Overall, a lavatory separate or in a bathroom for every six (and part of six) bedrooms. On each floor where there are three or more bedrooms, a lavatory	Overall, a lavatory separate or in a bathroom for every five (and part of five) bedrooms. On each floor where there are three or more bedrooms, a lavatory	Overall, a lavator separate or in a bathroom for eve (and part of five) bedrooms. On ea where there are th more bedrooms, a lavatory
6. GENERAL SHOWER/ BATHROOMS SERVING BEDROOMS WITHOUT PRIVATE FACILITIES	At least one bathroom Overall, a warm bathroom or shower-room for every six (and part of six) bedrooms	At least one bathroom Overall, a warm bathroom or shower-room for every six (and part of six) bedrooms	At least one bath Overall, a warm bathroom or shower-room for six (and part of si bedrooms
7. PRIVATE SUITES	Not required	Not required	Not required
8. TOILET FACILITIES FOR NON– RESIDENTS	Separate ladies' and gentlemen's lavatories and washing facilities with hot and cold running water, soap and towels. The gentlemen's may be located outside	Separate indoor ladies' and gentlemen's in addition to those serving the bedrooms	Separate indoor l and gentlemen's i addition to those the bedrooms
9. LIFT	Not required	Not required	To be provided hotels with three or more above n entrance

ACCOMMODATION SERVICES IN HOTELS

★★★★	★★★★★	☆☆	☆☆☆	☆☆☆☆
bedrooms to vide private ities. A ximum of 1/3 y provide a wer in lieu of a h A maximum of private showers y be provided in 9 bedroomed el	All bedrooms to have bathrooms, a reasonable proportion of which should additionally provide a shower	A bath or shower in 80% of the bedrooms	A bath or shower in every bedroom	All bedrooms to provide private facilities, half of which must have baths. Drip dry facilities
t required	Not required	Overall a lavatory separate or in a bathroom for every five (and part of five) bedrooms. On each floor where there are three or more bedrooms, a lavatory	Not required	Not required
t required	Not required	A warm bathroom or shower-room for every 5 bedrooms without private facilities	Not required	Not required
be available	To be available	Not required.	Not required.	Not required
arate indoor ies' and tlemen's in lition to any ving the drooms	Separate indoor ladies' and gentlemen's in addition to any serving the bedrooms, with cloakroom attendants for ladies and genglemen	Separate indoor ladies' and gentlemen's in addition to any serving the bedrooms	Separate indoor ladies' and gentlemen's in addition to any serving the bedrooms	Separate indoor ladies' and gentlemen's in addition to any serving the bedrooms
be provided in els with three els or more ve main rance	To be provided in hotels with three levels or more above main entrance	Not required	To be provided in hotels with three levels or more above main entrance	To be provided in hotels with three levels or more above main entrance

that the old-type 'nurses' home' is not now flexible enough to meet the demands of different grades of staff and that housing which is designed in detail for one particular grade or group of staff is un-economical, even though it is expected that the bulk of the accommodation needed will be for the nursing staff.

Basically, accommodation is needed for:

1. Student and pupil nurses undergoing basic training to whom permission to be non-resident is not given.
2. A proportion of qualified nurses undergoing post-certificate training.
3. A proportion of qualified full-time nurses – about one-third of the staff.
4. A small element of administrative and domestic staff.
5. A high proportion of house officers and registrars and a necessary minimum of more senior medical staff.

Staff can either be provided with hostel-type accommodation with full board and lodging or be given, on a rental basis, accommodation provided by the hospital in which they are able to live privately and undertake their own 'housekeeping'. Accommodation should be adaptable so that it can be used for either alternative depending on the staff need.

Particular attention has to be paid to sound insulation; siting should be in a reasonably quiet position with staff dining-rooms near by and not so widely dispersed that communal facilities have to be duplicated. Rooms used by medical staff must have reasonable access to wards and accident and emergency departments.

The Ministry recommend that there should be six *scales of accommodation* with scale A, B, and C not self-contained and scales D, E and F as self-contained units.

Scale A

For student nurses, domestic staff, and other junior groups of staff paying similar charges for board and lodging. They will require a separate bed-sitting room for sleeping and studying which will be furnished with, amongst other things, washing facilities and built-in wardrobe in which to keep clothes and other personal belongings.

For every four to six people, there will be one bath or shower, one W.C., one kitchen/utility room, and some provision for the storage of boxes and cleaners' equipment.

The gross area will be 24·15 m² (260 ft²) of which the bed-sitting area will be 11·15 m² (120 ft²).

Scale B

For staff nurses, house officers, pupil midwives, and similar grades.

They will have a separate bed-sitting room, but the bathroom, W.C., and kitchen/utility room facilities will be shared by only three or four people.

Instead of a central common-room, they will have the use of a smaller sittingroom shared between a few staff.

The gross area will be 27·41 m² (295 ft²).

Scale C

For sisters, senior house officers, and other similar grades. Each will be provided with a bedroom and a separate living-room; bath, W.C., and kitchen facilities will be shared between two people.

The gross area will be 41·34 m² (445 ft²).

Scale D

For deputy and assistant matrons, registrars, and similar grades. Each will be provided with a small self-contained flat consisting of a bedroom, living-room, bathroom and W.C., and kitchen.

The gross area will be 58·06 m² (625 ft²).

Scale E

For matron and other senior staff, a four-roomed flat will be provided. This type of accommodation will also serve for some married staff who need to be resident and have families or dependents living with them.

The gross area will be 82·68 m² (890 ft²).

Scale F

This is based on a self-contained two-bedroomed flat to be used by either married staff with one child or single staff with a dependent or similar grades.

The *additional accommodation* to be provided for Scales A, B, and C would be a central laundry-room, provided there are not fewer than 50 staff; and, where there are more than 100 residents, sick bay facilities should be provided.

The building notes recommend that the basis for the provision of scales A, B, C, and E types of accommodation be a three-bedroomed flat in which the partitions can be re-positioned as required (*see* Figure 1.8).

This comprises a living-room, dining/kitchen, three bedrooms, W.C., and store with a total area of about 74·32 m² (800 ft²) net, i.e. excluding common access space.

Common-rooms can also be provided in the flat areas or in a separate building, at the scale of 0·93 to 1·86 m² (10 to 20 ft²) per person, the higher rate being used for small numbers of staff. As an example, where there are 20 staff 37·16 m² (400 ft²) might be provided; but where there are 100 staff only 101·48 m² (1 200 ft²).

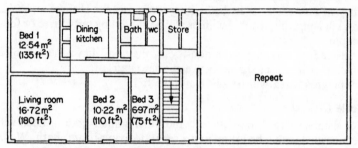

Typical floor plan of a four-room flat in a three-storey staircase access block

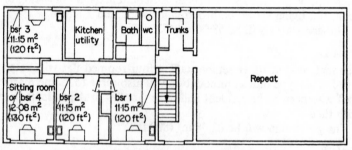

A four-room flat divided to provide four bed-sitting rooms

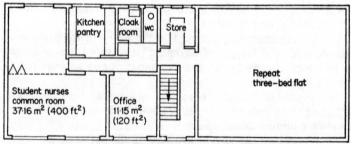

A four-room flat divided to form recreation space and office at ground-floor level

FIGURE 1.8   Lay-outs of a four-room flat divided for
different grades of hospital staff
(From *Residential Accommodation for Staff*, Hospital Building
Note 24, Ministry of Health, 1967.)

Other central provision includes laundry reception, a visitor's cloakroom, and an office for the warden or clerk which should be near the common-room, with the G.P.O. collecting and delivery point based on the warden's office.

The hospital authorities stress that accommodation must be planned so that changes in occupancy can be achieved, housing designed only for one particular grade of staff being uneconomic.

HOUSING FOR OLDER PEOPLE

The Ministry of Housing and Local Government have several publications which are of help when considering the special problems involved. These are listed in the reference section at the end of this book.

Nearly one-sixth of the population in Britain is over 65 years of age and it is considered that there is a marked need to help both single older people and couples to continue to live independently, even when they become less active. Local authorities are encouraged to provide accommodation which is mid-way between self-contained flats and houses and hostel care and to offer smaller flatlets which are labour-saving but in which there is some form of general over-all supervision. This they do by providing a bed-sittingroom with small kitchenette and with shared bathroom and toilet accommodation (*see* Figure 1.9). Blocks should not be so large as to become impersonal or institutional, but they have to be economic; a workable scheme needs a minimum of twelve flatlet units and a maximum of twenty-four to thirty-six units with a resident warden in charge. In these blocks, some self-contained flatlets for couples can be incorporated.

Siting

This should be central and not cut off from the communal life of the neighbourhood nor far from shopping areas. Flats should be sheltered, with a reasonable amount of sun, have a pleasant outlook, and be free from excessive noise.

Management

As the residents become less active, some will require a certain amount of assistance, and emergency help must be available in the event of illness or accident. Communal rooms, corridors, bathrooms, and W.C.s have to be cleaned, normally by the warden.

Standards of Accommodation

The Ministry's manual '*Housing for Special Purposes*' recommends that the desirable area for a single bed-sittingroom is 13·01 m²

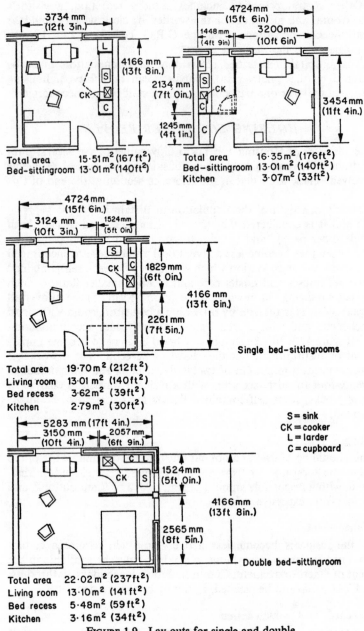

FIGURE 1.9 Lay-outs for single and double
bed-sitting – for older people
(From *Flatlets for Old People*, Ministry of Housing and Local
Government, reprinted 1962.)

(140 ft²) for use for living and sleeping with an extra 2·79 to 3·72 m² (30 to 40 ft²) added for the cooking area; this to be done either in a small separate kitchen or in a large ventilated cupboard which is cut off from the living-room by folding-doors (*see* Figure 1.10). The minimum area for a double bed-sittingroom should be not less than 18·58 m² (200 ft²) but a desirable standard would be 20·44 m² (220 ft²) which would include a bed recess which should have separate ventilation. A separate kitchen should always be provided.

Whichever type of accommodation is offered, the following suggestions are made:

1. Doors and windows should be so arranged that the bed can be conveniently placed and good use made of the walls.
2. To avoid excessive heat loss, windows should not be too large.
3. Window-sills should be low enough to enable a person sitting in an easy-chair to see out.
4. Fastenings must be easily accessible and the window must have some form of night-vent operated by a wheel-pulley and cord.
5. There should be a good central light and points for a bedside lamp and a wireless. Socket outlets should be 127 to 229 mm (5 to 9 in.) above the floor.
6. An electric bell near the bed and one in each bathroom should connect with the Warden's flat.

Kitchens

These should have a sink, draining-board unit, and small electric cooker. There should be storage space and a small ventilated food cupboard with shelves within easy reach and not more than 1·829 m (6 ft) above the floor.

Bathrooms and W.C.s

There should be not less than one W.C. to every two occupants and one bath to every four occupants, but if a convenient grouping cannot be arranged one bathroom may serve up to six flatlets. One bathroom on each floor might contain a drying or airing cabinet. Hand-rails should be fitted to the bath and by the W.C.

Ancillary accommodation

Warden's flat

This is considered an integral part of the block of flatlets rather than a separate house or flat, the size depending on whether it is the policy to employ a single person or a married couple.

Communal Sitting-room

It is suggested that an allowance of about 1·86 m² (20 ft²) should be

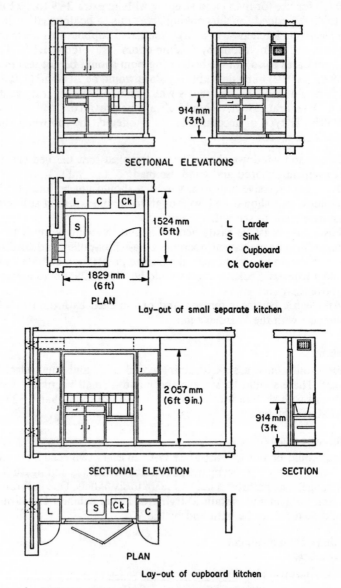

SECTIONAL ELEVATIONS

L Larder
S Sink
C Cupboard
Ck Cooker

PLAN

Lay-out of small separate kitchen

SECTIONAL ELEVATION   SECTION

PLAN

Lay-out of cupboard kitchen

FIGURE 1.10   Lay-outs of small separate kitchen and
cupboard kitchen – for older people
(From *Flatlets for Old People*, Ministry of Housing and Local
Government, reprinted 1962.)

sufficient for each person but that the room should not be too large to give a bare, cheerless, and homeless impression. Even though central heating is provided, it is pointed out that an open fire – using smokeless fuel – does a great deal towards helping a friendly atmosphere to develop.

Larders

It is advisable to provide a small well-ventilated room with slate slabs for keeping perishable food. This should face north or east and be convenient for each floor or group of flatlets.

Goods delivery room, laundry facilities and a guest room available for friends and relations should also be considered.

Circulation space

The architect should aim at as low a percentage of circulation space as possible. The recommended width for corridors is from 1·372 to 1·524 m (4 ft 6 in. to 5 ft) but this depends to a certain extent on whether rooms are planned to be on both sides or one side of the corridor. Where it is possible, corridors should have natural lighting and ventilation; staircases should be 'easy going', with handrails fitted here and in corridors.

Fire Escape

This depends on local authority regulations and may vary.

Heating

Central heating as background heating with, usually, a small electric fire fitted to a wall as secondary heating.

2 GENERAL MAINTENANCE

IMPORTANCE OF PERIODIC SURVEYS

THE proverb 'a stitch in time saves nine' is very apt when talking about the maintenance and running costs for any building. Repairs are expensive but are frequently avoidable as extensive structural damage is often the result of poor maintenance caused by either lack of knowledge or a policy of restricted expenditure.

Most damage is caused in some form or other, through water which will affect plaster and decorative finishes and ultimately causes fungal attack on woodwork, or through insects and rodents. It may be impossible to prevent the start of damage or infestation but, by regular external and internal surveys of the property, any such harm can be limited to a small area and not allowed to spread.

It depends on the age and type of construction how detailed and thorough the survey should be; it may be necessary to instruct a local building contractor to report on the state of the roof, flashings, and chimneys, or an electrician on the state of the electrical fittings. However good the survey is, it will not be able to cover all possible sources of trouble, such as collapsing drains; for these events most firms have a contingency allowance.

Programmed maintenance normally refers to the 4 or 5-year schedule for renewing external paintwork, for the internal redecoration of the building, and for the planned replacement of the electrical wiring and pipework, and the inspection of the building structure. This ensures that the provisional costs can be included in the revenue estimates and can be balanced one year with another. Each department will know in advance how they are affected and can plan accordingly.

Maintenance is normally done in the summer and is preceded by a general survey of the building to see the extent of any snow or gale damage or other deterioration. Again, in the autumn, an inspection should be made to ensure that all the required work has been completed and that all gutters, roof gullies, and grids are clear of leaves and twigs, that down-pipes are intact, and that the building is in a sound condition. As water and penetrating damp cause most damage, the best time for an external survey is on a wet day when any potential source of trouble can be clearly seen; a dry day can be used to inspect the property at leisure.

A survey should not be left to a handyman to carry out as he is not always able to judge the importance of long-term remedial action. He should however be expected, as a part of his duties, to notice and report on damage or areas which need attention; it should also be part of his duties to keep roof gullies and gutters clear, provided they are accessible, and to do general outside maintenance work.

DAMP

Damage can be caused in many ways – by rising damp which comes from the ground into the walls of the building, by penetrating damp caused by rain being driven into the brick and stonework by strong winds, by rain water seeping through faulty roofs and gutters, by leaking pipes either internally or externally and by excess condensation.

As damp can cause considerable damage to walls and ceilings and is also the cause of dry and wet rot, it should always be treated as soon as possible.

RISING DAMP

Every wall of a building which is in contact with the ground is fitted with a damp-course to prevent moisture harmfully affecting the interior of the building. The damp-course must be not less than 153 mm (6 in.) above the surface of the ground and is made from an impervious material of either two or more courses of slate, a layer of 1·8 kg (4 lb) sheet lead, asphalt, or layers of fibre felt, asbestos, or lead base, which are saturated in and placed between two layers of bitumen. Dampness will occur if there is any break in this barrier or if the ground level has gradually risen above it through gardening and rockery building or building operations. If the latter is the cause of dampness the remedy is to lower the ground level.

When faulty, the damp-course can be replaced by removing the broken parts and inserting a new course, a slow and difficult process.

A newer method is to stop the capillary action of the water rising through the porous brickwork. As it rises, the water produces a small electrical charge; the difference in the potential of this charge between the surface and sub-surface water molecules causes surface tension which helps the water to rise higher and more easily through the brickwork. If this small electrical charge is eliminated the rising damp can be stopped.

A method has been developed which earths the charge through a continuous copper wire. Wire is inserted in the wall at damp-course level by removing the mortar between the bricks, drilling at regular intervals, and mortaring the looped copper strips into position. The strip becomes part of a system of connected electrodes which are earthed, through junction boxes, with copper-covered steel rods driven into the ground (Figure 2.1).

This method can be used in all types of buildings irrespective of wall thickness; it is effective only against rising damp and will not prevent dampness from other causes. It may be necessary to install it on both internal and external walls.

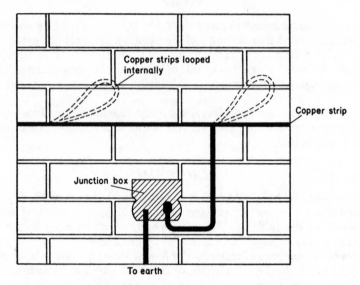

FIGURE 2.1   Copper-strip damp-course inserted in a brick wall

PENETRATING DAMP

All external walls will absorb moisture but they should be so constructed that penetration through to the interior wall is prevented. Cavity construction with two single layers of brick separated by a 50 mm (2 in.) cavity or air-space is sufficient to prevent rain penetration and will also provide some thermal insulation (*see* page 58). The cavity must extend at least 153 mm (6 in.) below the level of the damp-course; and damp-proofing has to be inserted at all places where doors or windows cross the cavity.

Damp can be caused by bad building when rubble or mortar has fallen into the cavity forming a bridge across – very difficult to remedy. The pointing between bricks and at window frames and doors may be weak; this can be remedied by re-pointing. Windows and doors, if wood, may be unprotected by paint or varnish and allow water to penetrate. To prevent this and to preserve the wood, external painting is carried out regularly at four or five yearly intervals, depending on the area and degree of weathering and exposure to which the building is subjected.

Where there is extreme penetrating damp, brick and stone can be protected by tile or slate hanging, by a cement finish which is pebbled or roughcast, or by use of a cement paint. The disadvantage of any such treatment is that the moisture will not be able to dry out through the external wall and will for a time continue to come through into the building.

FAULTY ROOFS

Roof leaks are caused by dislodged or cracked tiles or slates. The roof is lined with thick roofing felt and this, to a certain degree, will stop rain or powdered snow being driven under the joints, but it will not be sufficient to stop a torrent.

The join between chimney, skylights, and attic windows and the roof is covered by a roof flashing which is usually of lead, zinc, or copper. This may become defective with age by either cracking or developing pin-holes or even loosening or blowing off.

Flat roofs

Flat roofs are constructed either of steel and reinforced concrete which is covered with asphalt and laid with a slight drainage fall and is normally leak-proof, or the roof may be constructed from layers of bituminous felt, asphalt, or sheet metal; this does not seem to be so permanent. This second type of flat roof cover must be fully supported and extra strength given if it is to be walked over. Movement between the supports and the surface felt or asphalt may cause cracks, as will shrinkage of any paint finish. Moisture trapped between layers of asphalt or bituminous felt will vaporize with excessive heat from the sun and blister the material, and eventually split the surface.

Minor repairs are effected by applying an extra dressing or layer of asphalt or bituminous felt.

Parapets surrounding a flat roof and all *chimneys* are damp-coursed to prevent water penetrating down into the building.

FAULTY GUTTERS, GULLIES, AND DOWN-PIPES

Gutters and down-pipes are normally made from cast iron and should be kept in good condition by regular cleaning and painting. Down-pipes should have a clearance of at least 32 mm (1¼ in.) from the wall so that the rear surface can be painted and also to prevent a build-up of rubbish behind the pipe which could cause dampness. Gutters, gullies, and down-pipes may all become choked with leaves, twigs, and the occasional bird's nest; they may become loose on the fixing brackets; down-pipes may crack. Any defect should be dealt with, as water running down brickwork will seep into the building, often appearing some distance away from the fault. In some cases, cast-iron pipes are being replaced by polythene piping which should require little maintenance.

Defective waste pipes

These are not so easy to find as the fault is frequently within the wall but the waste pipe is suspect if damp appears at ceiling height near to the pipe and there is no apparent other cause.

Defective water pipes

A major leak soon becomes obvious; a minor leak may be running for some time before it is seen and may be difficult to trace. Whether damp is coming from a water pipe or is from some other cause can be determined by listening to the pipes using a stethoscope – a service which is provided by most Water Authorities.

There is always the risk of fractured water pipes if they have been allowed to freeze during cold weather.

CONDENSATION

This is caused by excess water vapour in the air cooling as it comes in contact with a cold surface; as the air cools, the vapour comes out of solution and condenses on the walls or floor. Steam from bathrooms and kitchens will increase the problem. Prevention is by adequate heating and ventilation, by the prevention and extraction of steam, and by providing warm and absorbent surface finishes. With more emphasis on the prevention of heat loss, double glazing, and draught exclusion, some buildings may suffer greatly from damp through condensation caused by insufficient through-ventilation (*see* Chapter 4).

Damp can also be caused by certain water-soluble salts which may be present in plaster or brickwork. These salts can extract moisture from the air at levels far below that of normal condensation and so cause areas of damp to appear on the wall. When these patches dry, the salts crystallize on the surface; if the fault keeps re-occurring the whole area may need stripping off and replastering.

As can be seen from Figure 2.2, damp can be caused by one or more of many different causes which may be difficult to define and remedy; but remedial action has to be taken as what might have been a small area of damage costing little to put right, if left may develop into a major undertaking.

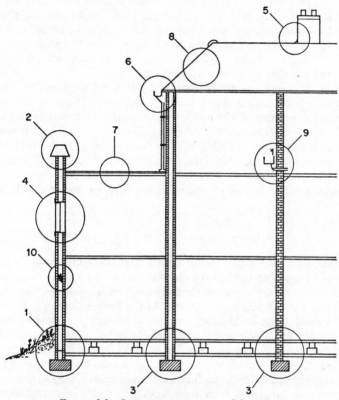

FIGURE 2.2   Some common causes of dampness
1. Ground level above damp-course
2. Defective damp-course at parapet
3. No damp-course on inner wall
4. Defective flashing at window
5. Defective flashing between chimney and roof
6. Defective gutter and down-pipe
7. Cracks in flat roof
8. Cracked and loose tiles
9. Leaking waste-pipe connection
10. Cavity bridge caused by mortar dropping on to wall tie

TIMBER DECAY AND ROT

Decay is due to the action of certain fungi which grow by feeding on the cellulose within the wood cell and leaving it in a dry crumbling state. Signs of attack are not always obvious as the growth is frequently on the underside of the wood and not seen, although in an enclosed space there may be a prevailing smell of toadstools. As the wood is affected it darkens in colour and will crack or fracture across the grain of the wood. Any timber which has been continually wet, damp, or flooded, and not dried out quickly is to be suspected as a possible site for dry or wet rot as the fungus is carried by the air from one building to another by microscopic spores, These will germinate and grow if they settle on any damp unprotected wood.

The main cause of timber decay is excess moisture in the wood. Properly seasoned wood in a building with central heating will have a moisture content of 10 to 12%; this moisture content rises to 14 to 16% where there is no central heating. Dry rot will only occur when the moisture content is 20% or over; and for wet rot the best conditions for growth are when the moisture content reaches 50 to 60%. It follows that where a building is well designed and constructed, with a good standard of maintenance, dry or wet rot will not occur.

DRY ROT (MERULIUS LACRYMANS)

Spores germinate under damp airless conditions and produce tiny strands known as hyphae which twist together to form mycelium. This is the vegetative part of the fungus which feeds on the wood and looks like thin whitish-grey sheets. As the fungus develops, it sends out special water-conducting strands which can penetrate through most walls and along beams and behind plaster. These strands carry moisture to previously dry wood so that the fungus is able to spread quickly from the original source of dampness. The fruiting sporophores, or bodies which produce millions of spores, vary in size from button-size mushrooms to pancake-like growths covering several feet.

Treatment

The source of damp must be dealt with. All decayed wood has to be cut out and burnt taking care not to distribute spores into new areas whilst so doing. A margin of at least 610 mm (24 in.) must be cut away beyond the infected area; where there are signs of the fungus on the plaster, this must also be removed allowing a margin of at least 305 mm (12 in.). Any walls or beams have to be scraped clean and sterilized by heating until the brickwork is too hot to touch, and treated with a fungicide whilst still warm. This should kill the remains of any spores of hyphae. New timber used for replacement should be treated with a preservative before being installed.

WET ROT (CONIOPHORA CEREBELLA)

Treatment

Treatment is similar to that for dry rot but sterilization of the plaster and brickwork is not necessary.

Dry rot causes most damage in buildings but wet rot is the most common fungus found, a recent survey indicating that it is present in over 25% of all houses in Britain.

WOOD-BORING INSECTS

Of these, the most common is *anobium punctatum* or the *common furniture beetle* which, in this country, accounts for 75 to 80% of all the damage done by wood-boring insects. *See* Figure 2.3.

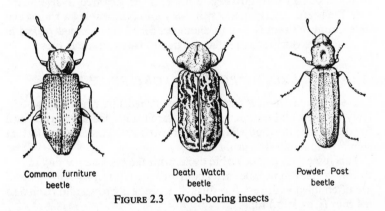

Common furniture beetle   Death Watch beetle   Powder Post beetle

FIGURE 2.3   Wood-boring insects

This beetle has a life cycle of from two to three years and will emerge from the wood generally from May to August. It attacks softwoods and the sapwood of hardwoods in structural timbers, furniture, and plywoods, usually after they have been in use for ten years or more. The boring is done by the larvae. There are four stages of growth: the eggs are laid in rough wood, in cracks or open joints in groups of three or four and they can just be seen with the naked eye. In a four to five week period an average of twenty to forty eggs are laid. These hatch in four to five weeks and the larvae start to bore into the wood in which they continue their tunnelling operations for the next two to three years. The larva then changes to pupa form and some six to eight weeks later will emerge through the flight hole; this is a circular hole 1·6 mm ($\frac{1}{16}$ in.) in diameter and is a sign that the beetle has *left* the timber, not entered it as is often thought. On sunny days, the beetle can be seen crawling on beams or ceilings or it will fly short distances. The adult beetle is 3 to 6 mm ($\frac{1}{10}$ to $\frac{1}{4}$ in.) long and reddish-black in colour.

A small pile of fine loose dust under furniture, woodwork, or in drawers or cupboards, is a sign of infestation, as are fresh exit holes.

DEATH WATCH BEETLE
(*XESTOBIUM RUFOVILLOSUM*)

This rarely, if ever, attacks wood which is free from fungus attack, the eggs being laid in wood which has already started to decay. The beetle prefers hardwoods but will also attack softwoods particularly if they are in close proximity. This is a larger beetle, being from 6·4 to 9·2 mm ($\frac{1}{4}$ to $\frac{1}{3}$ in.) long, and dark chocolate-brown in colour with patches of short creamy-yellow hairs. The life cycle is similar to that of the common furniture beetle but extends to three to five years, with the beetle emerging in April, May, or June, leaving a round exit hole about 3·2 mm ($\frac{1}{8}$ in.) in diameter. Small bun-shaped pellets in the fine bore dust indicate that the death watch beetle is present.

LYCTUS POWDER POST BEETLE

These are found in new partly seasoned or recently dried hardwoods. Only the sapwood is attacked as the starch is needed to provide food for the larvae; in wood which is old or well-dried there is insufficient starch to maintain the grubs.

This insect has a shorter life cycle, with the beetle emerging in one to two years. Flight holes are about 1·6 mm ($\frac{1}{16}$ in.) in diameter and are often filled with very fine dust. The beetle is brown and from 5 to 6·4 mm ($\frac{1}{5}$ to $\frac{1}{4}$ in.) long.

Another species of the powder post beetle is the *Bostrychidae* which is found in warmer countries or in woods imported from West Africa.

TREATMENT

Where the wood has been badly weakened it must be cut away and replaced with new timber which has been treated with a preservative. The most convenient treatment is to spray, brush, or inject insecticide solution in all parts of the furniture or structure which show signs of infestation and in all rough parts and backs of drawers or cupboards or other furniture. Two treatments are usually given in the spring and early summer and these are followed by another application the next year for the common furniture beetle and for the next four years in the case of the death watch beetle. Dust and cobwebs should be cleared regularly as these encourage and offer protection to the eggs and beetles.

Regular inspection of woodwork is always advisable.

WOOD PRESERVATIVES

Wood preservatives for use against decay and insects are of three types:

TAR OILS

Creosote has been used for over a century and is very effective. Its disadvantages are that the creosote can spread into other woods and stain plaster or paper with which it is in contact. It is not possible to paint over and so it is unsuitable for any work which is to be finished; it has a strong smell which also makes it unsuitable for indoor work and for any places where food is used or stored.

WATER-BORNE PRESERVATIVES

These consist of various chemicals such as salts of copper, chrome, zinc, sodium, mercury, and potassium dissolved in water. These have no smell, do not stain, and may be painted over if needed.

ORGANIC SOLVENT-TYPE PRESERVATIVES

These consist of chemicals such as the chlorinated phenols which are dissolved in a solvent, usually white spirit, solvent naphtha, or one of the petroleum oils.

The type of preservative which is most suitable will depend on conditions and the type of decay or infestation. Specialist advice should always be sought in any case where extensive damage is evident.

INFESTATION

RATS AND MICE (the rodent family)

As both rats and mice are nocturnal they are quite likely to be unnoticed unless there is a heavy infestation. Their presence should always be watched for; the main signs are:

1. The presence of droppings.
2. Gnawing, particularly around door and window frames, skirting boards, insulated pipes and electrical fittings, and in stores where packaged foods and sacks of flour, oats, etc., may be damaged.

3. Smell.
4. The presence of rat runs and tracks. Rats are short-sighted and follow well-determined paths keeping along pipe runs or to the edge of rooms; this leaves a dirty greasy mark from their bodies along the wall.

All rodents have incisor teeth which grow about 127 mm (5 in.) each year and are kept to a reasonable length by continuous gnawing. Control has been practised in this country from the time of Elizabeth I when a bounty of 1d was offered for 'the heades of everie three rattes or twelve myse.' The average life expectancy of both rats and mice is one year, in which time a rat can wean successfully about 20 young rats and the house mouse can raise 30 to 35 small mice. It follows that a small isolated infestation can quickly grow to alarming proportions.

Apart from the chaos they cause with female staff, the main reason for urgency in destroying all rodents is because they attack, contaminate, and waste vast quantities of food. They cause extensive damage to the structure of a building by gnawing wood, water-pipes, electric cables, and plaster-work. Damage may be done to drains and sewers by the common rat as it burrows between pipe joints causing them to collapse. They are the cause of the spread of many diseases, mainly typhus, rat-bite fever, Weil's disease, and ringworm. Rats are also credited with the spread of the great plague which decimated the population of Europe and Asia in the Middle Ages.

Treatment

Rats are quick to associate illness with their food supply so, when *poison* is laid, pre-baiting is essential. *Anti-coagulants* differ from most other poisons in that they kill only after repeated consumption, with the illness symptoms slow to appear and not associated with food. The anti-coagulant prevents the clotting of blood – by interfering with the production of prothrombin – and death is due to internal or external bleeding from damaged capillaries. An anti-coagulant is much more effective with rats than with mice who are sporadic feeders. Some rodent colonies have built up an immunity to anti-coagulants so poisons or other methods have to be used. Other ways of control are constantly being experimented with; these include putting down doses of the 'pill' in rodent bait, using high frequency levels of sound, and fumigation. The old-fashioned mouse or rat trap can still be effective when baited in cellars or outbuildings.

The Health Department at the local Council Offices usually have their own Rodent Exterminator or Rat-man who will give advice and provide the best methods of control for the area although, when there is an extreme infestation, it may be necessary to employ a firm specializing in the problem.

Any poisons used should be coloured and kept where it is quite impossible for them to be mixed with or come in contact with any food, utensils, or stores, or to be placed where they might harm domestic animals. Control by cats should be avoided as these create a health hazard if the cats are allowed where food is either prepared or stored.

INSECTS AND PESTS

A large number of different types of insects and pests can and do gain access to buildings, particularly when food and water are available. The presence of rubbish, refuse, and scraps of food, dirty drains, and cracks and cavities behind pipes or cupboards are an open invitation to any insect to set up a comfortable home life.

Good housekeeping is the most effective method of control.

Flies

Rubbish, decaying foods, and farm manure are typical breeding places from which a wide range of micro-organisms can be carried on the hairy legs of a fly and deposited on food or other surfaces. A fly feeds by first moistening the surface of the food to soften it before eating. Flies can disperse over a very wide area; some recent studies have tracked blow flies from their source to a point 28 miles away during a five day period. Effective fly control should cover the entire neighbourhood.

Control

(*a*) All refuse and refuse containers must be kept tightly covered, and drains and all potential breeding areas clean.

(*b*) Electrocution. Fluorescent tubes are used which give ultraviolet 'black light'. This attracts flies and other insects which fly towards it and are electrocuted by a grid. The flies and flying insects fall into a collection drawer at the base of the fitting.

(*c*) Spraying. Here care is needed to see that food, tables, and utensils are not contaminated.

(*d*) Insecticide lacquer. This can remain partially effective for several years. Microscopic crystals of insecticide on the surface should kill any insect with which it is in contact.

(*e*) The provision of screens to doors and windows.

Cockroaches

There are several species in this country. The German cockroach, or steamfly, is a more agile climber than the common cockroach 'blatta orientalis' so treatment methods will differ. There is also a much larger species which originated in America the 'periplaneta americana'. The common cockroach is said to have been introduced through commerce in the sixteenth century and was at first found only in the sea-port towns but now has a world-wide distribution.

Cockroaches can remain undetected for a long period. They are nocturnal and forage for food at night when they can be seen when the lights are switched on before they disappear rapidly into the nearest crevice. Their flattened bodies enable them to live in very narrow cracks. They like warmth and are found under radiators, hot water pipes, between skirting boards and the floor, under sinks and baths. They find their food by smell and will eat anything, paper, whitewash from the wall, books, materials, and most foodstuffs.

The harm done is not only caused by the amount which they eat but also the amount they spoil as they leave their excreta and 'roachy' flavour on food.

Control

(*a*) Sealing all cracks and crevices by cementing or re-pointing brickwork, tiles, and gaps behind pipe-work.

(*b*) Cleanliness, behind equipment, under sinks, and inside drawers and cupboards.

(*c*) Spraying on to smooth surfaces. These sprays kill by contact through the action of oils and chemicals.

(*d*) Insecticide powder. Fumigation. Insecticidal lacquer paint.

Silverfish

These prefer dark moist conditions and starchy foods.

Control

Insecticide powder, sprays, lacquer paint.

Ants

There are two types which can cause trouble: Pharoah's ants which are very small (2 to 3·6 mm in length) and of a light yellow colour; these are attracted by high temperatures and moisture and are often found where food is stored. Their food preference is for jams, sugar, honey, meats, fats, and cheese. Their nests are often inaccessible being located under floors, in walls, behind stoves or hot-water pipes, but their trails from the nest to their food supply usually follow well-defined paths. Disease is spread owing to their habit of visiting and walking through damp spots such as drains and lying water.

Black garden ants can also be a great source of annoyance as they will find their way in great numbers through any minute cracks towards their food supply.

Control

Any contaminated food should be destroyed. When possible the nests should be destroyed.

The area of infestation should be sprayed with an insecticide or an insecticidal powder should be used.

The Infestation Control Division of the Ministry of Agriculture, Fisheries and Food has some very helpful publications and will give advice where there are specific outbreaks of infestation.

Bedbugs

Bedbugs are reddish-brown and about 5·6 mm long and 3·2 mm wide. Unable to fly, they are brought into buildings in luggage which has been in an infested area, or else they can find their way into premises by crawling along pipes and through small cracks in doorways. Being nocturnal, they are often only detected by their habit of biting and sucking human blood. Eggs are laid in crevices in wood or plaster or behind pipes, wallpaper, or skirting-boards.

Treatment

By spraying with an insecticide. By sterilising bedding and other fabrics; this may be arranged by the local Public Health Authority who will also advise on fumigation.

Where there is a bad infestation, it may be necessary to strip the room of all wallpaper and panelling before fumigation.

Fleas

Fleas may be accidently brought in by domestic animals or by vermin.

Treatment

By spraying.

3 ELECTRICITY AND LIGHTING

BASIC ELECTRICITY

EVERY time an electric fire or lamp is switched on, often many miles away, a machine will generate the small amount of additional electricity that is needed to produce the heat or light required. When the heat or light is no longer required, the machine or generator will slow down and produce that much less electricity. There are two kinds of electricity in use – direct current (d.c.) and alternating current (a.c.). D.C. electricity can be stored in wet or dry cell batteries but the A.C. that is used for the bulk of domestic and industrial purposes has to be generated, as it is required, by the power stations. Electricity is transmitted from the power stations into the national grid which distributes it to towns and industrial centres and eventually into individual homes and factories wherever it is required. To supply any establishment or any domestic appliance wires are needed to carry the electrical current to and from the appliance; this is a *circuit*.

CONDUCTORS AND INSULATORS

Electricity passes through some substances easier than others; the best *conductors* are metal, carbon, water, earth, and the human body. *Insulators* prevent the passage of electricity; the main insulators are porcelain, rubber, air, and plastics.

Left to its own devices, electricity will take the shortest route to earth; so to prevent this all conductors are well insulated, usually with rubber or plastic. The insulation on a circuit can perish or deteriorate with age, heat, or through mis-use; so it is necessary to have all house-wiring checked at intervals of 15 to 20 years. This is often done before any large-scale re-decoration work is undertaken.

MEASUREMENT OF ELECTRICITY

The pressure of the electricity supplied is measured in *volts* (abbreviated as V); in the U.K. this varies between 200 and 250 V. The voltage of the electricity supplied by the local Electricity Board is recorded on the meter which is installed to record the amount of power used. An appliance is designed for a certain voltage range. Power is

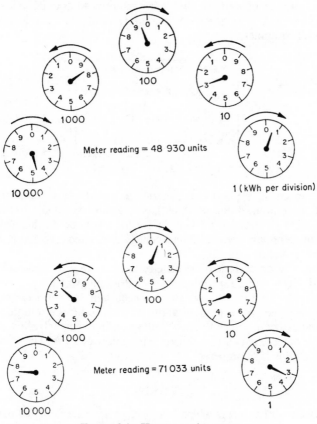

FIGURE 3.1 How to read a meter
The difference in consumption between the two readings = 22 103 units.

measured in *watts* (abbreviation W) and is recorded on the meter as *units* of 1 000 *watts* (a kilowatt, kW). Electricity is charged for by the unit which is the standard set by the Board of Trade as the amount of work done by 1 000 watts of electricity in one hour – a kilowatt-hour (kWh).

In large concerns, meter readings are taken monthly and a record of the consumption is kept.

TO READ A METER (*see* Figure 3.1).

When the dial hand is pointing between two numbers the smaller number is read; if the hand is exactly on a number then the number is read but when the hand is between 0 and 9, 9 is recorded.

The number of watts or the power required to operate any appliance varies and is recorded on the *rating panel* (*see* Figure 3.2) which is on all equipment.

```
XX  X  XX brand electric kettle

Capacity  - 3·4 cubic decimetres
                    (6 pints)

Voltage   - 200-240

Watts     - 3000
```

FIGURE 3.2   A rating panel

For example, a 1 000-watt electric fire would use one unit of electricity each hour. A kettle which has a loading of 3 000 watts would use 3 units of electricity if kept in use for one hour. In this way, the cost of using any piece of equipment is calculated (*see* comparative costs for fuel on page 74).

The flow or current of electricity is measured in *amperes* (often called 'amps' but abbreviated A). For example, water flows through a pipe which allows 2 litres to pass each minute, but a larger pipe with the same pressure might allow a flow of 4 litres a minute; similarly with a constant pressure or voltage, a thin wire will allow a flow of 5 A of electricity and a thicker wire a flow of 13 A. The measurement of this is in amperes.

FUSES

Every circuit has a *fuse* which is a piece of fine wire designed to carry only a certain number of amps. This is inserted in the circuit either in the plug connecting the appliance or in the fuse-box near the main switch. If there is any fault on the appliance or in the wiring and the current is more than the circuit can carry, the fuse will over-heat first before the main wiring and 'blow' or melt away so breaking the circuit and stopping the flow of electricity.

Installed by the Electricity Board is the *main fuse-box* and the *main switch* which enables the current to be disconnected from the mains supply when necessary. From the main fuse-box are fitted the distribution fuses which split the electricity into the various sub-circuits which are required in the building.

CIRCUITS

Older buildings are still wired for *power plug circuits* in the *distributive system* with each socket wired separately to the fuse-box (*see* Figure

3.3). This meant that the number of sockets was restricted to the size of the fuse-box and that the installation charges were high. Socket sizes varied from 2 to 15 A.

The *ring circuit system* (*see* Figure 3.4) is now being installed in all

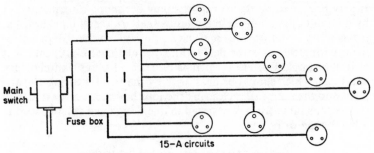

FIGURE 3.3   The distributive system of wiring

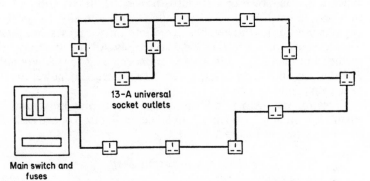

FIGURE 3.4   The ring circuit system of wiring

new buildings and when old buildings are re-wired. It is easier and cheaper to install – and to extend – this system, as each plug and socket is controlled by its own cartridge *fuse* which will 'blow' when any fault occurs but will not affect the rest of the circuit. All sockets are wired for 13 A.

The size of cartridge fuse or fuse wire for any piece of equipment is calculated by dividing the wattage required by the appliance by the voltage. This gives the amperage for the fuse. For an example:

An electric fire, 3 bars, is rated at 3 000 W. With the voltage at 240 V, it uses $12\frac{1}{2}$ A. This would require a 13-A fuse. In the same way, a polishing machine using 450 W would require a 2-A fuse in the plug. In this case it would be unsafe to use a 13-A fuse as this would remove the safety factor.

The wiring is *over-loaded* when appliances with too high a loading are used on a circuit. The 3 000-W fire must not be used on a circuit designed for 5 A as this might cause over-heating of the wiring and result in fire. With the increased use of adaptors in bed-sittingrooms there is a risk of over-loading any circuit.

The 'blowing' of a fuse indicates a fault somewhere on the system. It may be caused by the wiring in a plug becoming disconnected or by a lamp bulb going; these are faults that are easily remedied, but if the cause is not obvious and may be a fault in the equipment or main wiring this must be dealt with by a qualified electrician. It is only the simplest of electrical repairs, such as plugs, lampholders, and fuses, which should be dealt with by the Housekeeping Department and then only after clear instructions have been given and with the responsibility for repair vested in one designated person, such as a handyman or porter.

EARTHING OF APPARATUS

When a fuse is blown or a circuit is broken, electricity will find its own way to earth by the easiest route. To obviate any danger this might cause, *earth wires* are introduced into the wiring system; these wires are only current carriers if a defect arises. All power circuits are earthed but lighting circuits, which are normally 2 to 5 A, are not. For this reason it is an unsafe practice to connect any power appliance to the lighting system.

Notes for Instructing Staff on how to wire a plug are shown in Figure 3.5, on how to repair a lampholder in Figure 3.6, and on how to repair a fuse in Figure 3.7.

Notes for Instructing Staff

HOW TO WIRE A THREE-PIN CARTRIDGE-FUSED PLUG

From 1971, all new electrical appliances in the U.K. have to be wired to the colour code which will become standard throughout Europe; previously, equipment wiring was as follows:

The *LIVE* wire was previously *RED* but is now *BROWN*.
The *NEUTRAL* or return wire was previously *BLACK* but is now *BLUE*.
The *EARTH* wire was previously *GREEN* but is now *GREEN and YELLOW STRIPED*.

If the wires are connected to the wrong terminals, the appliance can become dangerous.

2-Amp fuses are used for appliances up to 480 W.
5-Amp fuses are used for appliances up to 1 200 W.
10-Amp fuses are used for appliances up to 2 400 W.
13-Amp fuses are used for appliances up to 3 000 W.

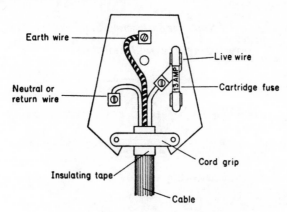

Diagram of a three-pin cartridge-fused plug

What to do	*Main points to mention*
Dismantle plug and remove fuse	
Cut away outer braid from cable and bind with insulating tape	Do not cut rubber insulation around wires
Fix in position under cord grip and tighten screws	This holds the wires firmly in place and prevents 'pull' at the terminals
Cut each wire so that it will reach round each terminal Cut back insulation 12 mm (½ in.) and twist the wire ends together	Terminals marked: E – Earth, L – Live, N – Neutral *Wire Colour Code:* *Brown* wire to *L* *Blue* wire to *N* *Green/yellow striped* to *E*
Connect to terminals and tighten screws	The insulation should reach almost to the connection There should be no stray strands of wire. *No* bare wires should touch
Replace fuse	Make sure it is the correct amperage
Replace plug top and tighten screws	
Report fault to the management	Safety: prevention of recurrence, repair of equipment, mis-use of equipment, etc.

FIGURE 3.5

Notes for Instructing Staff

HOW TO REPAIR A LAMPHOLDER

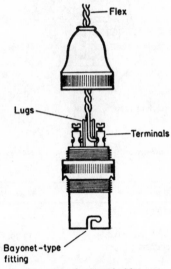

Diagram of a lampholder

As this in on the lighting circuit, there is no earth wire

What to do	Main points to mention
Switch off circuit at fuse-box before opening it	Safety. How circuits are labelled
Dismantle lampholder and replace if necessary	Where replacements are kept. Use a step-ladder
Thread flex through top of lampholder	
Untwist flex, cut away about 7 mm (¼ in.) of the insulation and twist the wire ends together	Do not cut wire
Connect wires to terminals	It does not matter which terminal
Tighten screws	Make sure no bare wires are touching
Hook flex under the small lugs	This takes the weight of the lampfitting and shade

What to do	Main points to mention
Screw down the top of the holder	
Switch on the electricity	
Report fault to the management	Reasons: safety, prevention of re-currence

FIGURE 3.6

Notes for Instructing Staff

HOW TO REPLACE A FUSE ON A LIGHTING CIRCUIT

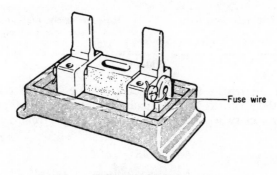

Diagram of a fuse

A fuse is a safety device to protect the wiring from damage if there is a fault in the wiring or if the current is excessive. It 'blows' either because of a break in the circuit or if the circuit has been overloaded.

In the fuse-box, each fuse should be numbered and a list kept of the lights and rooms controlled by each circuit. This list is usually attached to the inside of each fuse-box and enables the blown fuse to be found and replaced quickly.

What to do	Main points to mention
Switch off electricity at fuse-box, before opening the box	Safety
Pull out broken fuse	Labelling of circuits
Check size of fuse-wire required	For lighting circuits, a 5-Amp wire is used; this is marked on the fuse. Safety; why the correct amperage for the wire has to be used
Loosen screws at terminals	But do not remove

What to do	Main points to mention
Remove old wire	
Cut new length and straighten	About 102 mm (4 in.) long
Insert through centre of fuse	
Twist each end ↻ round terminals	Do not over-stretch wire
Tighten screws	This also tightens wire
Replace in box	
Switch on electricity	
Report fault to management	Reasons: safety, prevention of recurrence, repair of equipment, etc.

FIGURE 3.7

Before all repairs to lampholders or fuses on the distributive system, the electricity for the circuit *must* be switched off and appliances *must* be switched off and the plug removed from the socket.

BATHROOMS

Because of the danger from electricity, plug points or sockets are never installed in a bathroom. All appliances must be permanently fixed away from the bath or wash-basin and out of reach of water or wet hands, and all equipment has to be earthed. The only sockets which are permitted are those used for electric razors. A portable appliance should not be used in the bathroom. Lights and other appliances are operated by means of a pull-cord from a ceiling switch or else the switches are placed outside the bathroom.

ELECTRICITY COSTS

Industrial and commercial concerns use a *Maximum Demand Tariff* for lighting and for most power circuits. There is also a *Large-scale Cooking Tariff* and, when electricity is used for heating in night-storage heaters and under-floor heating, an *Off-Peak Tariff* is used. For comparative costs *see* Chapter 4.

The *Maximum Demand Tariff* is in two parts:

1. A heavy monthly, quarterly, or annual charge is made in respect of the maximum rate at which current is used at any time during the period.
2. A low rate is charged for each unit used during the period.

This system is intended to reflect the costs involved in providing electricity, a large part of which arise from 'peak' demands. From the consumer's point of view it means that the charge for electricity is at quite a low rate *provided* the maximum demand is controlled and not allowed to rise abnormally for short periods. This means some control in usage, as a cold February day may bring all available heaters into use with the total number of units used increasing by one-third or even a half of normal usage. The maximum demand is recorded on the meter.

The *Off-Peak Tariff* provides electricity at a low charge but only during set 'off-peak' periods.

LIGHTING

There are two types of light in general use, the filament lamp and the fluorescent tube, each working on a different principle.

FILAMENT LAMPS

These consist of a coil or coils of fine tungsten wire, which are supported in the centre of a glass bulb filled with an inert gas such as argon. The gas reduces the rate at which the tungsten evaporates. To produce the white light that is needed, electricity is fed through the wires until they glow white and a temperature of over 3 000°C is obtained. In time, this heat will cause a plastic lampholder to become brittle and will cause the convected hot air to mark the ceiling above the lamps.

Under the British Standard Specifications 161, a lamp should have an average life of 1 000 hours but this time will be shortened if there is any vibration, if a lamp of the wrong voltage is used, or if the mains electricity supply pressure should vary. Long-life bulbs are more expensive but should last for 2 000 hours. Rough service bulbs should be bought for lifts or for any area where there is much vibration; these do not give as much light but do last much longer.

Lamp sizes are standardized with the 25 W, 40 W, 60 W, and 100 W all of the same size, and the 150 W slightly larger. All fittings are bayonet type but the 150 W size can also be bought with a screw-in fitting.

The usual bulb finishes are pearl, white, or clear. Pearl is best for general purposes as it gives a soft light; white is softer than this but gives rather less light; whilst the clear bulb gives a harsh light which is more suitable for use in concealed fitments.

The *cost* of use is small. A 100-W lamp burning for 10 hours will use one unit or a 1 000 watts of electricity costing under 3p. This cost is negligible in a small house but can be expensive in a large building when innumerable lights are left burning. Lights must, however, be left on in corridors, stairs, and lifts for safety purposes.

FLUORESCENT TUBES

These have no filaments; instead the tube is filled with low-pressure mercury vapour. The electric current arcs through the tube causing the mercury gas to emit ultra-violet radiation which in turn bombards the fluorescent lining of the tube and makes it glow. These tubes cannot be plugged straight into the mains supply but need control gear or a starter switch to keep the current arcing steadily along the tube. The advantages of fluorescent tubing are:

1. The average life of the shorter tubes is 5 000 burning hours and for those of 1·2 m (4 ft) and longer an average of 7 500 hours; but this will only apply if the tubes are not constantly turned off and on. They should be left on for three hours or more each 'start', so when economy is needed the light should not be switched off if the room is empty for only a quarter or half an hour.
2. They are about three times more efficient than a filament lamp and, consequently, cheaper to use. A 1·2 m (4 ft) 40-W tube will produce as much light output as a 150-W filament lamp.

From the housekeeping point of view, the disadvantages are:

1. They are normally wired in batteries of four or eight tubes controlled by one switch. Some tubes flicker incessantly when 'going' and the only remedy is to turn all off until the one tube can be replaced.
2. Most staff can replace a filament lamp with the aid of a step-ladder, but tubing is often in recessed fitments and the replacement can require two men with two step-ladders for a considerable length of time.
3. More storage space is required than is needed for filament lamps.

Colour

Care must be taken with the colour so that replacement tubes match the colour of the other tubes in the room. There are about ten colours ranging from white, daylight and natural, through to de luxe natural (*see* Chapter 6).

Ultra-violet or black light is produced from a tube where special glass cuts out all but the invisible ultra-violet rays. This is used when fluorescence is incorporated into the materials used for steps, flooring, or other fittings. The ultra-violet causes them to glow so that staff are able to move about freely without the need of a bright light which might disturb residents at night.

LIGHTING REQUIREMENTS

Lighting requirements and standards vary tremendously. The recommended allowances are suitable for the younger generation with good eyesight. Those who are older will need more light for equal comfort. This is because the lens of the eye becomes less adaptable as it ages.

The unit of illumination is the *lumen per square metre* which measures the light output of an electric bulb or fluorescent tube. The level of illumination is measured by the number of *lux per square metre* as the light falls on a horizontal surface at table height.

A moderately bright day in summer produces about 5 000 lux, moonlight is about 1/5 of a lux whilst a well-lit road system is likely to be between 10 and 20 lux.

The Illuminating Engineering Society recommend the following values for:

general office work	—	400 lux
casual reading	—	200 lux
concentrated, close work	—	1 000–1 500 lux

General lighting recommendations are for:

function-rooms for banquets or dinners	—	100 lux
bars	—	50–70 lux
restaurants	—	100 lux
kitchens	—	200 lux
lounges	—	200 lux
bedrooms, corridors, and stairs	—	100 lux

with the provision of higher light levels where needed in such areas as selling and display points, at reception desks and counters, above mirrors and above beds.

These values are very much affected by the colour of the room furnishings. Dark colours in carpets, curtains, or walls will all absorb light whilst light colours reflect; so that if it is decided to change the decor of a lounge from pale beige to the traditional club-type furnishings of brown leather chairs and sensible brown carpets it will be necessary to increase the light source, possibly by the use of extra portable lamps.

A very rough guide in assessing lighting requirement is as follows:

100–150 watts from a filament lamp or 25–30 watts from a fluorescent tube will both produce 400 lux per square metre of floor area. Six hundred lux is produced from 150–200 watts from a filament lamp or 37–45 watts from a fluorescent tube. These figures can only be very approximate depending on the amount of light absorbed by the light fitting and the height of the fitting.

Consideration must also be given to the colour of the furnishings, to the spacing and overlap of the light source, and to any reduction of light owing to the age of the fitting and discolouration due to dust and dirt.

GLARE

This must always be avoided. Direct glare is caused by the contrast between the lighting source and its surrounds or the contrast between a bright sunny day and a low light source inside the building.

Glare can be reduced by:

1. Increasing the light to reduce the contrast.
2. Shading the window which admits the bright sunlight.
3. Darkening the wall by the window to reduce the contrast.
4. Increasing the angle between the source of glare and the line of vision.

Reflected glare from shiny surfaces such as walls and ceilings can be reduced by:

1. Reducing the brightness of the light source.
2. Screening the light by shades or concealed fittings.
3. Reducing the contrast by increasing the level of lighting.
4. By using matt wall and ceiling finishes.

CHOICE OF LIGHT FITMENTS

There is a vast choice of pendant, wall bracket, recessed, and portable fitments and some time devoted to the study of maker's catalogues or in the light-fitting department of a large departmental store or manufacturer can be well spent (*see* Figure 3.8).

A catalogue will specify the over-all size for height and width and the type of shade and lamp required for a particular fitment. The correct size of lamp *must* be used as otherwise, if too high a wattage is used, overheating of the fitting or scorching of the shade will occur. Heat-resistant wire at the entry point of a filament lamp fitting should be used.

Fitments are usually chosen for their decorative appearance and the lighting effect they produce. A proper impression can only be gained when they are lit and when visualized against their background. The amount of upward, downward, and sideways light must be considered and also the colour of the different surfaces in the room

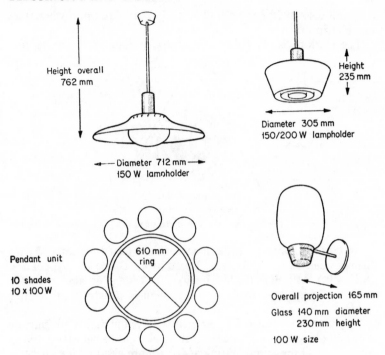

Height overall
762 mm

Diameter 712 mm
150 W lampholder

Height
235 mm

Diameter 305 mm
150/200 W lampholder

Pendant unit

10 shades
10 x 100 W

610 mm
ring

Overall projection 165 mm

Glass 140 mm diameter
230 mm height

100 W size

FIGURE 3.8 Light fittings

as the fittings will appear brighter against a dark background than in a lighter room.

Fitments must be considered for:

1. Durability and finish of the materials.
2. The inclination of the surfaces and corners for dust collection.
3. The ease of replacement, particularly when glass shades are used, as window-cleaners' ladders and spring-cleaning operations can be disastrous.
4. The temperature reached by the fitting, especially the lampholder, after prolonged use with the wattage recommended.
5. The weight. Will it be necessary to have the ceiling strengthened?
6. Any limitations of use such as depth of recess required, burning position of the lamps, or the fixing position.
7. Ease of replacement for lamps or fluorescent tubes. Is the shade so narrow that it is difficult to get a hand in to replace the bulb?
8. Ease of cleaning.

Portable lamps, when used, should be stable and not easily knocked over. Flexes should be non-trailing and not in a position where they can be tripped over.

The Mark of Safety which is illustrated in Figure 3.9 indicates that

The mark of safety

FIGURE 3.9   The mark of safety

an electrical appliance has been successfully tested for safety by the British Electrical Approvals Board for Domestic Appliances (B.E.A.B.). As well as the black-on-yellow triangular label, the mark is also permanently affixed to the appliance, usually on the rating panel.

Appliances are tested for electrical safety, the ability to function without giving the user an electrical shock, and to withstand abnormal electrical pressures. Wiring and earth are assessed for safety.

Portable appliances are also tested for stability to ensure that they do not easily fall over or overturn when used.

Heat should not be transferred from the heat source to any switches, knobs, handles or metal surrounds so that the appliance can be picked up and handled without danger of burns to the user. A durability test is also applied.

4 HEATING, INSULATION, AND VENTILATION

HEATING REQUIREMENTS

In the U.K. where the climate can only be described as variable, most heating installations are designed to heat a building over a range of 19·4 degrees C (35 degrees F); that is, with an outside temperature of, for example, minus 1°C (30°F), the installation will produce sufficient heat to bring the inside temperature to a comfortable 18°C (65°F). When the outside temperature drops to minus 8°C (18°F), it will be unlikely that the heating plant will be capable of excess capacity and will be unable to maintain a temperature of 18°C inside the building. The consequence is that one is met with a constant cry of 'isn't it cold' and 'something ought to be done about it . . .' This can be particularly annoying when various bedroom windows are found to be thrown open to the cold frosty air.

Most establishments regard *central heating* as *background heating* and cater for the more arctic conditions with some means of *secondary heating* in the form of a vast assortment of plug-in or fixed radiators, convectors, or fan-heaters.

It is accepted that some sort of heating will be needed in Britain for an average of 33 weeks each year when the difference between the outside and indoor temperature exceeds 10 degrees C (18 degrees F).

Agreement on the temperature for a comfortable working environment can be hard to get as standards vary tremendously, and in places where there is central heating, the acceptable temperature becomes gradually higher.

Living-rooms, offices, and similar rooms are preferred at 18 to 21°C (65 to 70°F), bedrooms at 13 to 16°C (55 to 60°F), workshops and other places where heavy work is carried out at 13°C, or for light work a temperature of 16°C.

In '*Residential accommodation for Hospital Staffs*', the Ministry of Health recommend that the background heating is kept to 13°C (55°F), and that the difference between this and the individual's requirements should be made up by the use of adequate secondary heating in each room. This heat is sufficient to keep the rooms aired and free from dampness and has the effect of cutting heat costs since many rooms are unoccupied for long periods owing to the staff working long and irregular hours.

The legal requirements for offices – under the Offices, Shops and Railway Premises Act of 1963 – is for a minimum temperature of 16°C (60·8°F) after the first hour. There is also the requirement that thermometers will be displayed.

HEAT TRANSFERENCE AND MEASUREMENT

The purpose of a good heating system is to produce and maintain a comfortable condition within the building when the outside temperature has dropped below the comfort level. To do this the heating engineer has not only to consider the temperature difference but also how to prevent loss of heat from the building into the outer environment. This necessitates close liaison with the architect at the design stage of the building.

Heat is *transferred* by:

1. Conduction

The transference is by contact. This varies with the material; metals and all dense heavy materials are good conductors, whereas light porous materials are bad; these are mainly the corks, wood, magnesia, asbestos, and glass fibre.

2. Convection

This occurs when a fluid, water or air, is in contact with a hot surface and expands resulting in an upward movement of the heated fluid to give up its heat elsewhere.

3. Radiation

This is the transfer of heat by a process similar to the radiation of light, the only difference being one of wave-length, radiation of heat occurring at longer wave-lengths. Like light, heat radiates in all directions, the amount of heat falling on an object varying inversely with the distance from the source.

Heating, insulation, and *ventilation* must all be considered as part of an over-plan in maintaining an acceptable environment within a building.

HEAT MEASUREMENT

At present heat is measured in British thermal units (Btu). One Btu is defined as the amount of heat required to raise the temperature of one pound of water through 1 degree F.

Since 1975, industry has changed to the *Système International d'Unités* (SI units) for all measurement. In SI units, heat is measured in the energy unit of the *joule*, so that where previously we measured heat in so many Btu/lb or gal in future the measurement will be J/kg or J/litre, the conversion rate being:

$$1 \text{ Btu/lb} = 2326 \text{ J/kg or } 2\cdot236 \text{ kJ/kg}$$
$$1 \text{ Btu/gal} = 232\cdot6 \text{ J/l}$$

Conversion for the Gas, Electricity, Coal, and Oil industries to the new units is dependent on legislation being passed by Parliament to amend the present laws governing weights, measures, and scales, which will permit the sale of fuel on a different basis.

HEAT LOSS AND INSULATION

Heat is lost from a building by conduction through the fabric, by convection, and by the loss of warm air escaping through doors, windows, and cracks.

Heat loss through the fabric of a building is measured by the *U value* which is the number of Btu that escape each hour through 1 ft^2 of the fabric for each degree of difference there is between the inside and outside temperature. The conversion factor from Imperial to SI units is 5·67, the Imperial units being multiplied by this factor to reach the SI value.

The better the construction the smaller is the U factor. Poor construction will give a U value of about 0·4 Imp. units (2·26 SI); better construction and good insulation can reduce this to about 0·2 Imp. units (1·14 SI) thus halving the heat loss. Norway and Finland with wooden houses, standard double glazing, and controlled ventilation have had for many years a U value of 0·10 Imp. (0·567 SI) or better.

In the past 30 years building styles have changed radically. Modern development in building has removed the necessity for thick external walls which gave good insulation and instead introduced framed lightweight structures with large window areas and a consequent increase in heat loss problems. Apart from heating difficulties in the winter, there is the reverse situation in the summer as many rooms become too hot owing to *solar heat gains*. This necessitates the installation of awnings or Venetian blinds to produce shade, or else air conditioning. The heat loss through the walls can be:

	U value	
	Imp. (Btu/ft^{2}h deg F)	SI (watts/m^2 deg C)
A 9 inch solid brick wall	0·40	2·26
An unventilated 11 inch brick cavity wall	0·30	1·70

	U value	
	Imp. (Btu/ft²h deg F)	SI (watts/m² deg C)
An 11 inch unventilated brick and clinker block wall	0·22	1·24
A large landscape window in a timber frame	0·80	4·53
A large landscape window in a metal frame	1·00	5·67

The heat loss through the roof can be of U value 0·43 Imp. (2·43 SI) or higher but, with a layer of impervious felt under the slates (this is now compulsory under Building Bye-laws) and with an insulating felt or quilt over the ceiling joists, this can be reduced to 0·16 Imp. units. A wood-block floor gives a U value of 0·15 Imp. (0·90 SI) whereas with a tile finish this is increased to 0·20 Imp. (1·13 SI). Little can be done to improve design and structure once the building is erected but some action can be taken to improve insulation and reduce heat loss.

Walls

Polystyrene bonded to a plasterboard or used as a lining 2 mm thick can be used under the wall-paper. This is a poor conductor of heat so provides a warm skin to the wall and has the added advantage of covering any cracks or irregularities and of reducing condensation. Wall cavities can be filled with fibre glass or rock wool to reduce heat conduction through the bricks.

Windows

A window pane will set up strong convection currents – and draughts – within a room (Figure 4.1). The glass is cooled by the outer air which, by conduction, transfers the heat loss to the inner side of the pane which sets up convection currents flowing down the window as the air cools. To stop this, radiators under the window should run for the full width; if less, the movement of hot and cold air is considerably increased.

Double glazing, i.e. two panes of glass in a window, can reduce the heat loss by more than half, provided that the window frames fit tightly with no cracks. The ideal distance between the glass is 19 mm (¾ in.), but frequently a smaller measurement makes it easier to fit the framings without making very much difference to the insulation.

Double glazing will also reduce condensation on the window but will not provide sound insulation which needs a space of 152 to 203 mm (6 to 8 in.) between the panes.

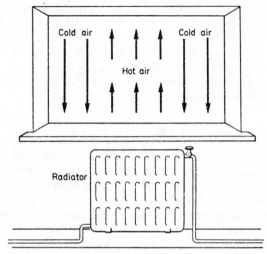

FIGURE 4.1 Air convection currents at a window

Roof

Bituminous insulating felt should be fitted under the slates or tiles of the roof and should be inspected regularly each year to make sure that it is still in position as it can be torn or damaged by high winds.

The ceiling must be insulated to retain the heat in the building. Bags of a 'loose fill' of rock wool, slag wool, gypsum, granulated cork, or fibre glass, are poured between the ceiling joists and spread evenly for a depth of 50·8 mm (2 in.); they must not be compressed but left loose. Overlapping blankets or quilts of rock, slag, or glass wool can also be laid loosely over the joints. They should be about 25 to 28 mm (1 in.) in thickness.

There must be *no* insulation *under* any *water tanks* or expansion tanks placed in the roof space as the heat from the building will prevent the water freezing in bad weather. Insulation for these should go over the top of the tanks, generally in the form of a movable box which is well insulated.

Draughts

These cause excessive ventilation and should be stopped. For *doors*, metal stripping is effective and permanent, and for revolving doors the manufacturers provide thick rubber and felt draught excluders which can be replaced when worn. In *windows*, draught frequently comes through gaps between the frame and the wall. These can be filled with plaster or putty, and painted over when dry. Wedges are invaluable with sash windows and will also stop the rattling which occurs with old windows. Where there are suspended wooden floors, draughts come between the *skirting* and the floor-boards. These can be stopped by fitting a wooden strip or coving to cover the join. In *chimneys*, draughts may be reduced by means of a chimney 'throat', but unused chimneys must never be completely blocked at room level unless they are also sealed off at the top as ventilation is necessary to prevent dampness occurring along the line of the flue.

SOLAR HEAT GAINS

To make the internal environment acceptable, solar heat gains must also be considered, particularly when air conditioning is being installed. Solar heat can become very troublesome in south-facing buildings with landscaped windows and it is often necessary to fit some type of sun control to reduce the amount of heat being radiated into the building.

There are three main ways of excluding heat. They are:

1. By intercepting the sun's direct radiation whilst admitting light from other angles. This is achieved by using external fittings such as awnings, blinds, and canopies, overhangs or projections, or vertical or horizontal louvre systems. As mentioned in *Principles of Sun Control*, 'one of the most effective sun shades, when it is practical, is a row of trees. Trees remain cool in sunny weather because of transpiration heat losses, and do not re-radiate by long-wave radiation. Deciduous trees provide shade in summer but admit sunshine in winter.' The use of external sun controls can turn away as much as 75% of solar heat as the absorbed heat is dissipated externally.

2. By reflecting back the infra-red of the sun's radiation by the use of heat-reflecting, heat-absorbing, or tinted glass. These are relatively ineffective, with heat-absorbing glass reducing the solar gain by only 25%, and stained glass by 30 to 65% depending on the colour. Double-glazing using ordinary window glass reduces the heat load by 10 to 20%.

3. By diffusing the radiation by using internal blinds and curtains; although it is difficult to reduce a room temperature by this method as much of the heat absorbed by the blind or curtain enters the room. Their best use is to reflect out as much radiation as possible by using material with a white face or by using one of the net curtaining fabrics which have been developed and which have an aluminium coating. This metallic finish can reflect up to 68% of the sun's radiation. In winter, the position is reversed and the amount of heat lost through the windows is reduced.

VENTILATION

A room is well ventilated when the air in it is fresh and pure and is sufficiently warm and dry for the occupants to be comfortable. Whilst it is desirable to eliminate draughts, as we have briefly mentioned, unless there is complete air conditioning installed it is important *not* to seal up the building completely.

Air is a mixture of gases: 20·96% oxygen, 0·04% carbon dioxide, 79·0% nitrogen, and a small quantity of inert gases and water vapour.

In a stuffy room, the oxygen content is never less than 20% and the maximum for carbon dioxide content should not exceed 0·06%. About 84·9 m³ (3 000 ft³) of air per person is needed every hour to maintain healthy conditions.

Good ventilation is *required* not only *to replace the oxygen* which is used in respiration and in combustion, but also:

1. *To prevent an unduly high concentration of moisture* from respiration and from the steam produced in kitchens and bathrooms. *Humidity* is the amount of moisture or water vapour contained in the air. At any given temperature, air can absorb a definite amount of water: when it has reached the maximum it can hold, it is said to be *saturated*. At high temperatures more moisture can be absorbed than at low temperatures. 0·03 m³ (1 ft³) of air at 27°C (80°F) when saturated will hold 158 grains of water but at 0°C (32°F) will only hold 27 grains, 7 000 grains being equal to one pound. Normally the water content is not high enough to saturate and the air only contains a proportion of the moisture which it can hold. This is expressed as a *percentage* of the *relative humidity*. When the temperature drops, or air comes in contact with a cold surface, the water vapour present can saturate and will appear as condensation on windows and walls. Water vapour on a very humid day has been known to short-circuit the lighting for fluorescent tubes.

   Any humidity in excess of 80 to 90% produces an extremely stuffy feeling, headaches, a disinclination to work, and a general loss of ease. This is because the human body loses the heat it produces mainly through evaporation from the skin. This occurs most easily when the relative humidity is about 50%; with a high humidity, this evaporation is slower and more difficult and the body over-heats. Conversely, too low a humidity can cause excessive evaporation from the body and can result in throat infections and a feeling of extreme cold. The object of most heating and ventilation installations is to achieve a relative humidity of 40 to 60%.

2. *To dispose of surplus heat* from both people and machinery. This is particularly necessary in halls and theatres. A person of average size in normal clothing, doing light clerical work, will produce about 139 W (475 Btu) each hour. Heavier work will produce 264 W (900 Btu) and much heavier work will produce 440 W (1 500 Btu). Where numbers of people are assembled for any length of time mechanical ventilation will be required as will a flexible heating system which can be switched off a short time after assembly.
3. *To reduce the concentration of bacteria and viruses* in the air, and
4. *To remove any smells* which develop when people are crowded together.

Most authorities consider that under normal conditions with single-glazing the natural ventilation that is obtained by opening windows and doors or by air leakage from closed doors and windows is sufficient; however in internal rooms without natural ventilation and halls or other rooms for large numbers mechanical ventilation is needed. If an open fire is used the rate of ventilation can be more than adequate. Where there are double-glazed sealed windows, there must be additional fresh air supplied by means of either mechanical ventilation or through an air-conditioning unit.

If there is *not* air conditioning, the Model Byelaws lay down that every habitable room must have at least one window with the opening portion at least one-twentieth of the floor area and the height of that portion at least 1 753 mm (5 ft 9 in.) above floor level. A room must be at least 2 286 mm (7 ft 6 in.) high; and where it is partly or wholly on the roof of the building, there shall be at least 2 286 mm (7 ft 6 in.) over not less than half of the floor area.

Rooms without a flue or fireplace *must* have some other forms of ventilation to compensate.

The minimum rates of fresh air are laid down by some authorities. Offices, living-rooms, and bedrooms will require 12·74 to 21·23 m³ (450 to 750 ft³) of air each hour; whilst halls, theatres, and cinemas will need 28·23 m³ (1 000 ft³) for each person. Where numbers are not known, ventilation standards are maintained by stipulating the number of air changes each hour.

The Ministry of Health's recommendations for nurses' accommodation suggest 2 air changes each hour for common-rooms, with 1½ air changes for bedrooms increasing to 3 air changes for sick bay accommodation. A large kitchen needs 25 to 40 air changes each hour to maintain adequate conditions. This can only be achieved by mechanical means.

Wall brick ventilation plus a free area with access to wind conditions will give the following:

6451·6 mm² (10 in²) air flow = 16·98 to 33·36 m³/h
(600 to 1 200 ft³/h)
19 354·8 mm² (30 in²) „ „ = 31·13 to 56·6 m³/h
(1 100 to 2 000 ft³/h)
32 258·0 mm² (50 in²) „ „ = 45·28 to 84·9 m³/h
(1 600 to 3 000 ft³/h)

depending on the speed of the air current.

MECHANICAL VENTILATION

The types of mechanical ventilators which are in general use are:

1. Simple extract and input fans

These are fitted to the windows and are driven by a small electric motor as a means of increasing ventilation by natural means. They collect dirt and grease quickly and should be cleaned regularly.

2. Plenum Ventilation, or warm-air heating

In this there is a central air intake through a plant or boiler house and the air is distributed by intake fans through ducts to where it is required, the air being frequently filtered and warmed before distribution. To increase the circulation, extract fans may also be fitted.

3. Air Conditioning

Air Conditioning is the term used when plenum ventilation is adapted to meet particular requirements, such as in a hot climate. As has been mentioned, the relative humidity of the air is important, and humidifying – or dehumidifying – chambers are fitted to adjust the percentage of moisture present to the required level. Air is heated by passing it through heating chambers. In hot climates, air is cooled by passing it through the same type of chambers which are cooled by a series of cold water pipes running from a refrigeration plant.

All air intake should be at a high level where the supply is considered to be most pure. All ventilation plants should be regularly maintained and cleaned in accordance with the suppliers' instructions. *See* also page 65 dealing with warm air heating and air conditioning.

As can be seen, determining the specifications for heat requirements is a highly skilled job and should be dealt with at the design stage of building. All that can be done in a book of this nature is to give some appreciation of the skills which are involved.

Heat requirements depend on the level of heat required, the construction of the building, and the manner in which it is ventilated, which is in turn dependent on the numbers using the building and the activities in which they are engaged.

TYPES OF CENTRAL HEATING

Central heating literally means the heating of a building from a central source but now also includes heating by such other means as storage heaters and electric floor warming. The main methods of heating are still, however, by the circulation of hot water through a system of pipes and radiators or the circulation of warm air through a series of air ducts and grilles.

CIRCULATED HOT WATER HEATING

A boiler, solid fuel, gas, or oil-fired, heats the water which then circulates through the building.

Gravity Circulation

Here the operation is based on the principle that hot water rising from the boiler in the *flow pipes* is lighter and less dense than the cooler water which falls and returns for reheating. This makes for an automatic circulation of water from boiler back to boiler in which very little can go wrong, but it does mean that:

(*a*) Pipes must be of sufficient diameter, over 69 mm (2½ in.), to allow for the free flow of water and there must be no resistance from friction or bends in the piping.

(*b*) the flow pipes from the boiler should rise as directly as possible to the highest point in the system before the water starts to drop through the radiators.

(*c*) all horizontal runs of pipe should have a downward slope in the direction of the return to the boiler.

The drop in temperature from boiler back to boiler may be as much as 18 to 24 degrees C.

This method of circulation is found in the older type of building erected more than 30 years ago and has been superseded in all new buildings by the following system.

Small Bore or Forced Circulation System

Here the circulation of the water is forced or maintained by an electrically operated pump through pipes of a much smaller diameter, or bore, 12 or 15 mm (⅜ or ½ in.) being quite usual.

The advantages are:

(*a*) The volume of water in the circuit is considerably less than for gravity circulation.

(*b*) There is a quicker circulation with a temperature drop of less than 5 to 6 degrees from boiler back to boiler.

(c) Because of (a) and (b) a boiler with a smaller heating capacity can be used.

(d) Installation is much quicker, easier, and cleaner as the installation pipes are so much smaller.

Water can be circulated in a number of directions (see Figure 4.2). From the housekeeping point of view, the direction of the circulation is unimportant until an air-lock occurs which usually happens after a period when the heating has been turned off. The hot water contracts on cooling and pockets of air collect in the spaces left which, if they are big enough, will prevent the circulation of water when the heating is restarted. If an air-lock occurs when the system is in operation, it is released at each radiator working in rotation along the circuit, starting with the radiator nearest the boiler and using a radiator key at the release valve.

The great *disadvantage* of all water-circulating heating systems is that they contain water and, even in the best of establishments, water can leak from joints or valves and cause damage. Under inclement weather conditions in exposed parts of the building even central heating pipes have been known to freeze. Many of us who have contended with the older type of heating system consider that the comparatively new methods of warm air heating and air conditioning have many advantages.

WARM AIR HEATING AND AIR CONDITIONING

Both are usually only installed in new buildings as the flow of air requires ducts built into the wall. As these ducts are of a larger cross-section than is needed for water-pipes, it is rarely possible to install them in old buildings.

With warm-air heating and ventilation, the supply air is usually delivered into a room at 60°C (140°F) and gives a room temperature which is affected by and dependent on the outside temperature – as it is with all forms of central heating. With warm-air heating, there is no humidity control.

Air conditioning is a system in which the desired conditions of temperature, relative humidity, and cleanliness of the air are maintained in a given space; it follows that the system must be able to supply air which is either warmer or cooler than the existing air. Conditioned air is usually supplied at a temperature of between 26 and 38°C (80 and 100°F) and cool air at 10 to 18°C (50 to 65°F) and at a relative humidity of 50%. As well as air ducted from a central unit (Figure 4.3), a window package unit is also available and is fitted when air conditioning is only required in certain areas (Figure 4.4).

In most systems, fresh air and returned air are mixed and passed

SERVICES AND MAINTENANCE

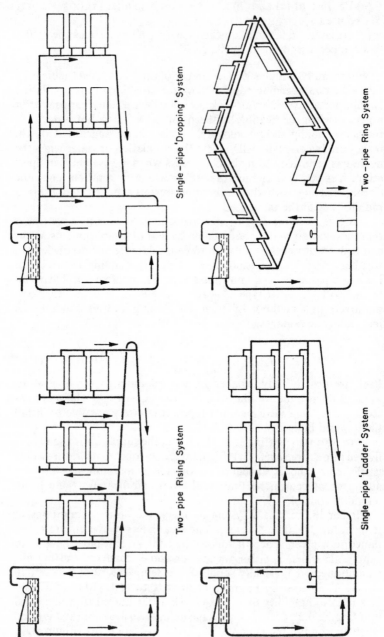

FIGURE 4.2   Some of the many arrangements for heating/radiator installations

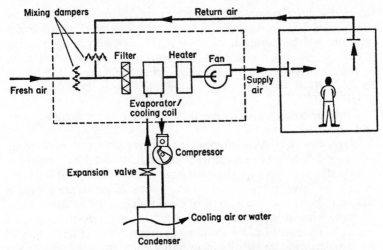

FIGURE 4.3 Simple single-zone air conditioning system
(From *Packaged Air Conditioning*, Air Conditioning Advisory Bureau.)

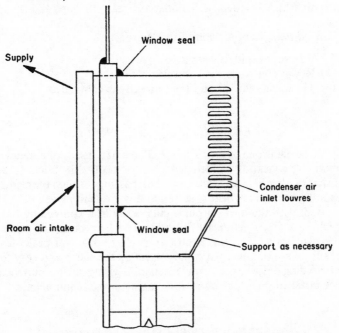

FIGURE 4.4 Air conditioning room unit mounted
in a window
(From *Packaged Air Conditioning*, Air Conditioning Advisory Bureau.)

through a filter which removes any particles of dirt. The air is then cooled by passing it through a cooling coil which also extracts moisture which is drained off. The air is heated by either passing it over a coil which circulates hot water or, in most small units and window package units, by direct action from an electric heater battery. When water heating is used, heating is by oil, gas, or electricity.

When air conditioning is installed, all windows are double-glazed and sealed.

Warm air can be directed into a room with either a downward or an upward flow. When the outlet is placed high on the wall or in the ceiling, dirt and dust deposits, which can occur when the air is drawn in at a low level, are prevented. The position of the return air grille has an influence on the pattern of air circulation which develops in a room. When it is placed at a low level, the air is drawn down, so preventing a layer of warm static air at ceiling level. Other factors to be considered are the development of draughts; low level returns are not recommended for commercial buildings, bars, or restaurants where they may become dirt traps or where it is undesirable to draw air which is laden with smoke or steam through the occupied area.

The *advantages* of air conditioning are:

(*a*) It is very rapid in operation.
(*b*) Room control is easy and flexible in use.
(*c*) The air is purified and the humidity is controlled.

ELECTRIC STORAGE HEATERS

The principle is one of heat storage. The unit consists of a metal case containing a heating element which is embedded in brick or other refractory material. An electric current, passing through the elements, heats the brick. This heat is stored and is gradually given off as it is required, with the heat output regulated by heat-controlling louvres which vary from gentle to full-heat. The heaters are operated by time-switches so that the electricity is charged at 'off-peak' tariffs, usually on an 8-hour night supply. Heaters are cheap and easy to install needing only the provision of separate wiring circuits and meters; once installed, there are no routine maintenance requirements.

ELECTRIC FLOOR WARMING

This is a similar system to the storage heaters but with the heating elements embedded in the concrete floor slab so that the floor itself provides the heat storage. In some installations, it is possible to with-draw the heating cables for maintenance when these are run through conduits. This system is also operated by time-switch, is completely automatic, and uses 'off-peak' electricity. This form of heating is very suitable for entrances and in public rooms where there is constant movement, but it can be tiring in places where people have to stand for any length of time.

With storage heating, there is a disadvantage of some lack of con-trol as, although heat emission can be reduced, it cannot be entirely prevented if the day unexpectedly turns hot. Ideally, heating require-ments should be known in advance.

THE SITING OF RADIATORS AND HEAT POINTS

All heating points should be dispersed to give as even a temperature as possible. This is best done by meeting the heat loss where it occurs at doors and windows. Radiators should be the same width as the windows to prevent draughts. Incoming air at doors is heated by ceiling or floor panels so that the air is comparatively warm and not uncomfortable. It is possible to install 'hot air curtains' which are as effective as a solid door but the high installation and maintenance costs make them impracticable for general use.

THE BOILER

This is a very expensive piece of equipment and in a large establish-ment will have a trained boiler-operator in charge. In a smaller establishment, the care of the boiler and heating system may be part of the duties of a handyman-porter.

The dividing line between domestic and commercial boilers is usually considered by the manufacturers to be 440 kW (150 000 Btu per hour).

All boilers require flues, normally of brick, which are lined with either salt-glazed ware or asbestos cement pipes. The best position for the flue is on an inside wall so that it is unlikely to chill and reduce the air-flue flow.

On a low pressure boiler, the *flow temperature* for the water leaving the boiler is usually 71 to 82°C (160 to 180°F) when the water is to circulate through radiators but is at a lower temperature of 49 to 54°C (120 to 130°F) when embedded floor or ceiling panels are in use.

Water is stored in a cylinder. This is defined as a cylindrical closed vessel capable of storing water under pressure greater than atmos-pheric pressure.

THE CYLINDER

The Cylinder is either direct or indirect.

Direct cylinder

All the water heated is stored in the boiler and used directly through the system as it is required. Water losses are made up directly into the boiler. A direct cylinder will only be met in the smallest of establishments as it leads to excessive 'furring' of the boiler and pipes.

Furring occurs where temporary hard water is heated above 60°C (140°F), when the calcium or magnesium bicarbonates, which are soluble in the water, are converted to insoluble carbonates. These settle and form incrustations or furring on the inside of pipes and boiler; the quantity depends on the degree of temporary hardness, the temperature, and the volume of water used. To prevent this occurring an indirect cylinder is used.

Indirect cylinder or heat exchanger

This is illustrated in Figure 5.3, page 81. It has two water circuits, the primary and secondary. Water in the primary circuit is continuously reheated and heat is exchanged by conduction with the water in the secondary circuit. By this means, the heated water in the boiler is only replenished when the boiler is drained down or when leaks or evaporation from the feed tank are made good. This prevents damage to the boiler and the constant need for descaling, although access canals or 'mud holes' are still fitted so that small deposits can be removed.

An indirect cylinder will still be fitted where there is a soft water supply as the action of dissolved air in the water causes steel and iron to corrode; because of this internal parts of the system are often rust-proofed before installation, a process in which the metal is raised to red heat and then treated with live steam.

Materials for pipes and cylinders are either copper or galvanized mild steel (covered by a British Standard) but in any system the metal used should be the same throughout as, with certain types of water, an electrolytic action is set up when dissimilar metals are used.

All boilers have a safety valve to let off excess pressure from super-heated water or steam and have a gauge which shows the recommended and the actual working pressures. These should be tested regularly and should work.

There is usually a separate *Insurance cover* for boiler installations in conjunction with specialist inspectors. The normal requirement is for the boiler to be opened for inspection about once a year and the cylinder opened every two or three years, but this is at the inspector's discretion and will depend on the age and condition of the installation. It must be remembered that the boiler may take one or two days to cool sufficiently before it is dismantled; so most inspections take place in an off or summer period.

The British Standards Institution lay down a colour code for Boiler House Piping (B.S. 1710).

Steam pipes are aluminium or crimson.
Central heating pipes below 60°C are French blue.
Fuel Oil (diesel) pipes are brown.
Boiler feed water pipes are light French blue:
Hot water supply pipes are eau-de-nil.
Compressed air pipes are white.

COLD FEED, VENT PIPES, AND EXPANSION TANKS

Since the water contents of a heating installation expand when heated above 4°C (39°F) it is necessary to provide capacity for the additional volume. This expansion is in the proportion of one gallon (4·55 litres) of water to every 23 gallons (104·56 litres). To take this overflow, an expansion tank is fitted above the level of the highest part of the system (usually in the roof), and is about one-third full when the system is cold. The tank is connected to the main supply and, by ball valve control, also replenishes any boiler loss which occurs through leakage or evaporation. A vent pipe releases air thrown out of solution.

A slight boiler leak, although undesirable, is of no immediate concern *provided* the ball valve is working correctly, and this should be regularly inspected. Where the water supply is reduced or disconnected for some reason, it may be necessary to let the boiler fire out immediately to prevent damage to the boiler and pipework, particularly on the hot water system.

All boiler-room pipes should be *lagged* or *insulated*, especially if they are in a draughty or exposed position, both to conserve heat and to prevent freezing. Insulation, however efficient, will not stop the flow of heat but will only retard it and, in cold-water pipes and others where the water is stationary over a long period, the contents will freeze if the temperature is below 0°C for a long period. The risk is greater for small-bore pipes where the bulk to be cooled is less in relation to the surface area. The ratio of water expansion on freezing is 11 litres increasing to 12 litres.

Materials suitable for insulating both *pipes* and *boiler* are magnesia, asbestos, glass fibre, and cork. Magnesia and asbestos may both be applied as a plastic composition; when they are applied surface damage is prevented by painting or coating the outside with a hard setting cement.

Pre-formed plastic sections, moulded to fit various sized pipes, can be used but are unsuitable for uneven or complex piping systems. Lagging will also prevent condensation within the building.

THE MAIN DUTIES FOR A BOILERMAN

The Main Duties for a boilerman will include:

The cleanliness of the boiler-house.
Recording of fuel consumption.
Maintenance of correct operating temperatures.
Daily, weekly, and monthly maintenance.
Correct receipt and storage of fuels.

TYPES OF FUEL

In 1956, the Clean Air Act became law. This empowers local authorities to declare certain areas to be smoke controlled, so that within these areas it is an offence to emit smoke from a chimney and it is necessary to use certain 'authorized' fuels. This provision can affect the choice of heating system. In England and Wales, the 'authorized' fuels are all types of coke, low volatile steam coals, anthracite, phurnacite, coalite, rexco, gas, and electricity. Oil and coal are not authorized fuels but may be used in equipment designed, maintained, and operated to produce no smoke. The onus is on the user: so users beware!

Oil, gas, and coke are the most usual fuels for large-scale use. Although electricity is used for the control of automatic or semi-automatic boilers, it is at present considered too expensive for the main source of heat unless used on a special 'off-peak' tariff for under-floor heating or for storage heaters.

OIL

Mineral oil is a natural fuel which is found underground and which, provided the right type of well is bored into the strata, will flow to the surface. It is mainly composed of hydrocarbons, some impurities, sulphur, and some incombustibles. The process of refining oil is basically one of distillation which results at the upper end of the scale in the petroleums and then in descending order, paraffin, gas oil, and the residual oils. It is the gas oils and residual oils which are used as furnace fuels.

Fuel oils are available in various grades; the lightest is gas oil, the heaviest being composed of the residual oils, and the intermediate grades being mixtures of the two. Only the lightest grades can be used with small domestic installations but as the installation becomes larger so it is possible to burn the heavier and cheaper grades.

Fuel oil has the merit of being very clean as regards delivery, storage, and handling, with no question of ash removal. As it is contained in storage tanks and pipe lines and can be automatically controlled, labour requirements are minimal. Oil has a high sulphur content and, although it may be easily burnt under smokeless conditions, any maladjustment of the burners can lead to a heavy dense smoke.

Oil-fired boilers are of two main types: atomizing and vaporizing using different grades of oil.

TOWN GAS

Town gas – and coke – is produced when a bituminous coal is heated in closed retorts. The volatile gases which pass out are purified, collected in gas-holders, and distributed in the local gas supply pipe network.

NATURAL GAS

Natural Gas is obtained, in the same way as oil, by drilling into the earth's strata. Its advantages over town gas are:

(a) It does not rely on coal as its source.

(b) No manufacture required, only purification.

(c) The calorific value is twice that of town gas. This not only automatically doubles the present pipe and storage capacity but also means that burners on all equipment require renewal and adjustment to acheive a burning rate equivalent to town gas.

(d) A very low sulphur content. This eliminates 'verdigris' copper sulphate deposits on equipment.

(e) It is free from carbon monoxide and is therefore non-poisonous; although if it is used in apparatus in which there is insufficient ventilation, carbon monoxide problems will still develop through bad combustion.

Gas has the advantage of cleanliness and general convenience in use, and of being easily adapted to thermostatic and time-switch devices; only routine attention is required. With gas there is no storage problem for the user.

COKE

This is produced from bituminous coal, from which the volatile gases have been driven off, the non-volatile part of the coal remains as the smokeless fuel, coke. This is then broken down into various sizes to suit the different types of boiler. Now that many of the local town gas works are closing as supplies of natural gas become more generally available, the future supply of coke is in some doubt.

Coke shares with anthracite the quality of being difficult to ignite but, once ignited, it burns easily with a good smokeless flame. With constant burning, clinker forms on the firebars and needs regular removal to ensure a clear bright fire.

Hand firing of the boiler is necessary as the coke is so abrasive that it is difficult to design a mechanical firing system; this leads to high labour costs.

Other disadvantages are:

(a) For good results, chimney and flues must be cleaned regularly.

(b) There is a high sulphur content. When the boiler is shut down, sulphur fumes can be produced which are unpleasant.

(c) There is a storage problem. Coke is bulky and dusty and should be kept dry for good combustion and to prevent condensation from forming in the flues. Stored in an open yard, it can become the deposit for waste or a home for mice and other rodents, neither of which is desirable.

OTHER MANUFACTURED FUELS

Other manufactured fuels include the semi-cokes, coalite, phurnacite, rexco, and other brands. Some of these are manufactured in special shapes, such as briquettes and ovoids, to make handling easier.

ELECTRICITY

Electricity is not strictly speaking a fuel but is a source of power. It is clean to use, available at the turn of a switch, and needs neither boiler, flue, fuel storage space, nor appreciable labour for its use, so is very convenient. Cost depends on the type of tariff charged – maximum demand, off-peak, or commercial.

COMPARATIVE COST OF DIFFERENT FUELS
(see Figure 4.5)

To compare the cost of different fuels, it is necessary to compare the different heat or calorific values and the efficiency of the apparatus in which it is burnt.

The calorific value is defined as the amount of heat energy which is released when burning a stated amount of fuel material. It has customarily been measured in Btu/lb and the ordinary commercial unit of heat, the *therm*, is equal to 100 000 Btu. This has now been replaced by the joule/kilogramme (J/kg).

$$1 \text{ therm} = 105 \cdot 506 \text{ MJ}$$

Fuel	Fuel cost	Gross heat value	*Apparatus efficiency	Net heat value	Cost per useful therm
Oil, atomizing	18.5p per litre	36 075 Btu per litre	75%	27 056 Btu per litre	68.4p
Gas, natural	35.2p per therm	1000 Btu per ft^3	75%	750 Btu per ft^3	46.9p
Electricity, Off-peak tariff	2.61p per unit	3412 Btu per unit	100%	3412 Btu per unit	76.5p
Day-time tariff	4.90p per unit	3412 Btu per unit	100%	3412 Btu per unit	142.3p

FIGURE 4.5   The comparative cost of different fuels

* Apparatus efficiency is assessed when the equipment is running at full load and is very dependent on the way in which it has been installed and the method of operation. The figures can only be approximate, with the seasonal variation in efficiency as high as 10 per cent. Note that the units can only be altered by Act of Parliament and no decision on metric equivalents had been taken when this book went to press.

SECONDARY HEATING

There is a very wide choice of 'fires' available for secondary heating using either gas or electricity, size and shape depending on circumstance, where they are to be used, and the amount of extra heat required.

Fires which light and give radiant heat should be fixed firmly as a wall fitting as this eliminates the danger of the fire being moved and placed close to curtains, against opened cupboard doors, or in a position where it can be knocked over. All types of fire *must* have a guard fitted. This is compulsory wherever there are children under 12 years of age, and it is also an advisable precaution where there are groups of people or numbers of elderly residents.

Where portable fires are required, the safest and most practical seem to be the convector or fan-heater type, with a suitable warning that these should not be covered. Fan-heaters have the added advantage that the heating unit can be turned off and the fan used for cooling purposes during the summer and in hot climates.

FUTURE TRENDS IN LIGHTING AND HEATING

Experiments which started in America and which are now continuing in the U.K. and Europe are based on the idea of using the surplus heat produced by both the lighting system and the people resident or working in a building as the main source of heat.

The standards of illumination in the USA are usually much higher than in the U.K. often reaching 1 500–1 800 lux. Since about 85% of the electricity used to produce this light is given off as a heat, it seems logical to harness this excess heat rather than let it waste. Each watt of electricity used for lighting generates 3·4 Btu/h.

The system works by using air and water heat-exchange units in conjunction with the fluorescent lighting tubes; the water is then chilled in a refrigeration plant and the heat extracted is channelled back through the central heating unit. To get the most out of this system, insulation standards must be very high. In one building in the USA, with a lighting level of 150 lumen/ft^2, the entire 33 stories are heated to a maintained temperature of 22°C (72°F) with an outside temperature of minus 10°C (14°F).

Another development is the use of a conducting paint which forms the heating element and gives warmth evenly from all over the wall. This paint, which can be sprayed or brushed on, is linked to the electricity supply by two strips of aluminium foil placed along the top and bottom of the wall. For safety the system runs at 40 volts so it is necessary to install a transformer to adjust the electricity supply. Normal decorations can be used over the paint.

5 PLUMBING

THE WATER SUPPLY

UNDER the Water Act of 1965, the water authorities are required to provide a supply of water which is pure and wholesome, that is, it must be free from any visible suspended matter, have no odour, taste, mineral matter, or bacteria which would be likely to cause disease or impairment to health.

Water is supplied by means of *distributing mains*. These pipes vary in size but are usually 54 mm (2 in.) and upwards in diameter and are laid at a depth of not less than 762 mm (2 ft 6 in.) below ground level and not less than 914 mm (3 ft) down if the pipe is under the roadway; this is to prevent damage from frost and heavy traffic. There are two types of supply, the most general being the *constant system* in which the mains are kept full and under pressure. Where it is necessary for the water supply to be periodically turned off, this is known as an *intermittent supply*. From the distributing main and smaller branch mains, a separate *service pipe* leads off and is required for each building.

A service pipe carries water and is subject to pressure from the main. Stop-valves or cocks are fitted at the start of each branch main so that water can be turned off with the least inconvenience to users. Where the service pipe crosses the boundary of a building, a stopcock is again fitted. The length of service pipe between the mains and this stopcock is known as the *communication pipe* and this, and the stopcock itself, is the responsibility of the local water authority. The section from this stopcock carrying the water on to the premises is the *supply pipe* and is the responsibility of the occupier of the premises.

Another stopcock is usually placed just inside the building so that if either becomes defective the water can still be turned off. Handymen and porters should know where this stopcock is; it should be serviceable and turn easily.

The supply pipe enters the building below ground level and rises along one of the internal walls so that it is protected from frost damage; if the pipe rises along an external wall it must be well insulated. Water pipes must be accessible and in modern buildings are generally in plumbing ducts. The supply pipe takes the water for storage to the cistern which is situated at a high level in the building, generally in an attic space. This height provides the pressure on the internal domestic supply. When the supply pipe rises to the cistern it is then referred to as the *rising main* (*see* Figure 5.1).

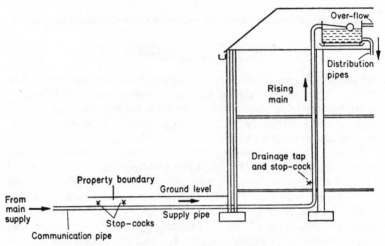

FIGURE 5.1   The water supply – from the mains

The *cistern* can be of any shape or size and may be made from zinc, iron, lead, copper, galvanized iron, and sometimes asbestos cement. To prevent damage from overflowing water, most have a metal tray fitted beneath them. They should be tightly covered; any ceiling insulation should not go beneath the tank but be incorporated in the cover to prevent any danger of freezing.

The water supply is controlled from the rising main into the cistern by means of a *ball-valve* (*see* Figure 5.2).

The main faults which develop in the ball-valve are:

1. Puncturing of the ball so that it fills with water and remains at the bottom of the cistern.
2. Corrosion or grit at the inlet pipe so preventing the valve closing tightly.
3. A faulty washer.

An *overflow pipe* to carry off surplus water must always be fitted and is fixed just below the level of the inlet pipe from the rising main. The overflow discharges through an external wall and serves as a warning when there is anything wrong with the supply system.

Stop-valves are fitted to each outlet pipe from the storage cistern and also to each pipe run so that sections can be isolated for repair.

Some bye-laws require that all water fittings and pipes should be fitted with a *drainage tap* so that the whole system can be emptied.

When pipes are repaired, care must be taken to ensure that dissimilar metals are not in contact with each other; with some metals such as copper and galvanized iron an electrolytic action is set up

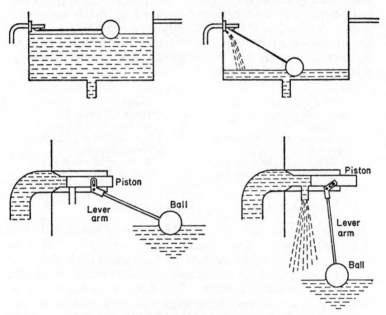

FIGURE 5.2 The ball-valve
As the water level drops, the ball also drops and the lever moves the piston out so letting water flow into the cistern. As the water level rises, the ball and lever move the piston against its seating and shut off the flow of water.

which causes corrosion. Some authorities allow polythene or plastic pipes to be fitted for the cold water supply; the danger in this is that the earth wire for the electrical wiring system or from the lightning conductor is often connected to metal cold water piping; if these metal pipes are changed to plastic the earth lead is then lost and a new one should be fitted.

Water enters the storage system through pressure from the mains supply but pressure is obtained within the building by the level of the head of water above the tap and the size of the connecting pipes. This is why the cold water cistern must be at the highest water level in the building.

From the cistern, water is supplied to the hot water system, cold taps, and water closet cisterns; drinking water pipes may occasionally be taken directly from the rising main and not pass through the storage tank.

MINIMUM REQUIREMENTS

When there is a constant supply of water, the storage capacity normally equals one day's consumption which for hotels and flats is usually estimated as 114 litres (25 gallons)' per person per day. The demand for water is constantly increasing, with as yet no corresponding increase in supply, so that wastage should be avoided. As a rough guide to its use we require for:

a bath 178 mm (7 in.) deep	–	114 litres (25 gallons)
a bath-full	–	159 litres (35 gallons)
a shower	–	23–36 litres (5 to 8 gallons)
a wash-basin (with the plug in)	–	7 to 9 litres (1½ to 2 gallons)
the cistern for a W.C.	–	9 litres (2 gallons)
for drinking, per head per day	–	1·35 litres (0·33 gallons)
for cooking, per head per day	–	2·73 litres (0·65 gallons)

HOT WATER SUPPLY

Maximum requirements depend on the number of basins, baths, and W.C. cisterns which are installed but the amount of hot water required will also vary considerably with the use of the building and type of residents. A hospital will need a constant supply throughout the day, a hotel will have demand from 6.00 p.m. onwards, whereas a student's residence may have its greatest need from 10.00 p.m. onward. A method often used to establish the size of the hot water storage cistern and the capacity of the boiler is to provide storage for twice the amount of water that the boiler can heat in one hour, although in a very large building only 75 % of maximum requirements may be allowed for. Methods of heating and types of boiler are dealt with in Chapter 4.

The amount of hot water required also depends on the temperature at which it leaves the boiler. This is usually set at 71 to 82°C (160 to 180°F).

The following are average temperatures for:

Cold water	4·4 to 7·2°C (40 to 45°F)
A warm bath	35·6°C (96°F)
A hot bath	40·6°C (105°F)
For hand-washing	43·3°C (110°F)
Washing-up	60 to 82·2°C (140 to 180°F)

If the hot water is at 71·1°C and the cold water at 4·4°C, a bath containing 100 litres of water at a temperature of 40·6°C will require

54·5 l. of hot water; it will need 59 l. if the hot water temperature is 65·6°C and 64·2 l. if it is only at 60°C.

The hot water distribution pipework is connected to the top of the storage cylinder (*see* Figure 5.3). To avoid large quantities of cold

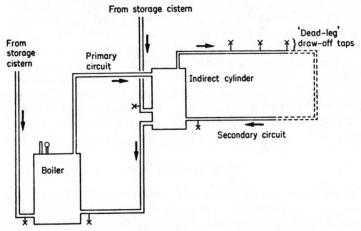

FIGURE 5.3   Indirect cylinder and hot-water circuit

water being drawn off before hot water is available a return pipe on the distribution system is introduced so that there is a continuous circulation to and from the cylinder. This avoids the wastage of both hot and cold water lying dormant in the pipes. This secondary circulation may be by gravity feed but more often than not will be by pump attachment. The piping from the secondary circulation to the draw-off point is known as the dead-leg, the permissible length of which is limited by the Water Supply Authority. In domestic use, the maximum dead-leg with a pipe not exceeding 22 mm (¾ in.) diameter is 12·192 m (40 ft).

The local Water Authority should be notified of any proposed alterations to the system but need not be notified for repair work.

WATER HAMMER NOISE

This can bring complaints from residents. It is caused by pockets of air which collect at high parts of the pipe run. When the water is turned off or when a ball-valve closes, the water which will not compress, surges back towards the air pocket which is compressed and then released. When there is more than one air pocket, they surge backwards and forwards – with the consequent hammer noise – and may continue for some time. The simplest cure is to turn a tap on to release the pressure; otherwise, it is a case of altering the fall on the pipe run.

Some authorities lay down *minimum requirements* for good bathroom and sanitary accommodation.

Since December 1975 a 5-star hotel must have 100% of their bedrooms en suite fitted with a private bathroom. The Ministry of Health recommend, for their most junior hospital staff, one bath or shower and one W.C. to each four to six people; the University Grants Committee have a minimum acceptable scale of one W.C. and one bath for every six students or one shower for every twelve students and one hand wash-basin for every three students. The Ministry of Housing and Local Government suggest that, when housing older people in flatlet accommodation, there should be not less than one W.C. to every two occupants and one bath or shower to every four.

THE BATHROOM

The basic requirement is for a room which is warm and comfortable and in which ideally there should be some form of heating even if only in the form of a towel rail. There should always be a hook, a rail, or a stool on which to place clothes and towels. The walls, ceiling, and floor should be such that they are unaffected by condensation and water; for this reason ceramic tiles, terrazzo, and laminated-plastic panels are often used for floors. Where there is this type of hard solid floor, a drainage grid is built-in so that, when cleaning, the room is simply mopped out. Other floorings used are vinyl and linoleum, although both are affected by water; and, for comfort, carpeting. Amongst the many types of carpet available, those with a sponge-rubber backing are the most suitable as they will not rot or shrink when wet.

Walls can be painted or panelled. Wallpaper is not advisable as it marks easily with the condensation. Curtains should be washable and absorbent or spongeable.

Where the bathroom has natural ventilation from windows and louvred fittings, this is usually considered to be sufficient; but when the bathroom is situated internally, some form of mechanical ventilation and air conditioning is essential.

BATHS

The standard size is 1·676 m (5 ft 6 in.) long by 711 or 737 mm (28 or 29 in.) wide, although both smaller and larger sizes are available. A smaller size is useful when space is limited, where one is dealing with young children, or if there is a limited hot water supply but it is not really adequate for adults. A larger size uses considerably more hot water from the supply.

Baths are made from porcelain-enamelled cast-iron or enamelled pressed steel; they are very heavy, being about 163·3 kg (360 lb) in weight, and this may mean that extra support has to be given to the flooring where several are installed. Recent developments are with moulded plastics and glass fibre, both of which are much lighter and can be installed by one man. These baths are warm to the touch but as they are flexible, they have to be well framed underneath to give support. Their advantage over enamelled baths is that the surface cannot chip or wear through and does not rust or stain from the copper or iron salts from dripping taps. With some plastic moulded baths, a cigarette stubbed out on the edge may melt the plastic.

When buying, the general appearance and finish should be noted. The base should be flat so that there is less risk of people slipping *but* there must always be a slight slope towards the plug so that the bathwater drains off completely. It is possible to buy a bath with a slightly roughened or moulded non-skid base or with strips inserted to prevent slipping. This is particularly necessary for older people; another solution is the provision of rubber mats, suction fitted.

Consideration must also be given to the position of a grip-bar, particularly for the elderly and the very young, and the position of soap ledges, waste, and tap fittings. It is normal to have the waste pipe at the same end as the taps but these can also be a side or corner fitting. To aid cleaning, bath side panels are always fitted.

In an hotel or hostel, it is sensible to have a fitting above the bath to take drip-dry clothing – even though a drying or utility-room is provided.

SHOWERS

Showers have the advantage that they take up half the space that is needed for a bath so that often a shower can be provided whereas a bath can not. They also require less hot water when used. Showers are usually installed in men's residences but, provided the shower-rose is on a side fitting and not centrally placed, they are equally convenient for male and female use.

The base is made from porcelain, enamelled steel, moulded plastic, or glass fibre. Normally 762 mm (30 in.) square, the tray is recessed; three sides of the enclosure are tile, mosaic, or other water-proof material whilst the fourth side usually has a door or curtain of plastic, nylon, or towelling. Curtaining is not ideal as it is frequently found to tear in use and, unless tucked in at the base, does not always keep the water-splashes under control.

BIDETS

Bidets are becoming increasingly used and are essentially for washing the lower parts of the body. It is a question for the local authority whether they are connected to the soil or waste-pipe.

HANDBASINS

For preference there should be a handbasin fitted in every room where there is not a private bathroom; so that the room can be used for general purposes, the basin is usually screened from sight in a cupboard fitting. This avoids congestion in bathrooms in the early morning and aids the letting of student rooms in residences for conferences and meetings during the vacation. The floor area requirements when basins are in a wash-room area are 0·93 m² (10 ft²) for each basin to allow for adequate access, but when the basin is used in a study-bedroom this is reduced to a basic 0·33 m² (3·5 ft²).

Basins should not be too small. They can be obtained as a wall or corner fitting to hold as little as 4·5 litres (1 gallon) of water but these are not convenient for normal use; for comfort, the basin should hold from 6·82 to 9·09 litres (1½ to 2 gallons) of water, with the surrounds draining easily into the basin so that soap in the recesses does not remain sodden. Taps should not project too far over the basin and can be fitted either to the wall or to the unit. Pedestal, frame-fitted, or cantilever models are available with the more modern cantilever fittings being the best for room cleaning purposes.

Jointing between bath, shower, or handbasin and the wall or surround is made with plastic fillers which eventually darken and crack allowing water to seep behind and under the appliance. It is sometimes difficult to get a tight joint; one method of avoiding this trouble is to fix the basin or bath into a plastic sheeting surround and join the two with a metal strip.

CLEANING OF BATHS, SHOWERS, AND HANDBASINS

This is done daily using a net cloth and a mild detergent and paying particular attention to the overflow, plug, chain, and waste grids, and around and under tap fittings. Basins are then rinsed and dried and the chromium fittings polished with a dry cloth. When finished, the plug and chain are left neatly by one of the taps.

Where a bath is discoloured, the stains can be treated by either rubbing with an abrasive or using a cut lemon dipped in salt or, where stronger measures are required, ¼ teaspoon of acetic acid in ½ cup of water or salts of lemon; this last is poisonous and should be used only by the Housekeeper. All in all, it is simpler to have a tap repaired promptly than to run the risk of staining.

TAPS

Taps are not sold with the bath' or handbasin but are bought as a separate item. They should be chosen for:

(*a*) Ease of working.

(*b*) Safety. The hot water tap should not become unduly hot when used; when the hot water flows through the centre of the handle it can become very dangerous particularly for children or older people (*see* Figure 5.4).

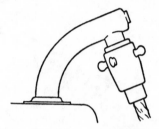

FIGURE 5.4   A hot-water tap which can over-heat

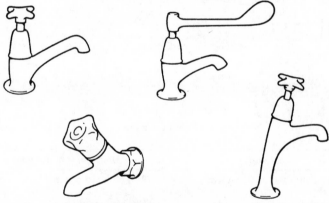

FIGURE 5.5   Other designs for taps

(*c*) Ease of cleaning, especially round and under projections and its position in relation to the basin surrounds and the wall (*see* Figure 5.5).

Hot water can be saved by the use of a spring return tap which incorporates an automatic device which turns the water off after a fixed period; if these are fitted, a notice should be displayed as, to the uninitiated, they can be disconcerting.

The water flowing through the tap is controlled by a washer which is made from composition or leather for cold water and a rubber composition for the hot water tap. With time, these washers become worn, and result in a dripping tap. Notes on how to replace a washer on a tap are set out in Figure 5.6.

Notes for Instructing Staff

HOW TO REPLACE A WASHER ON A TAP

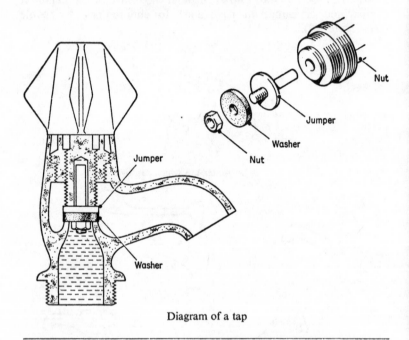

Diagram of a tap

What to do	Main points to mention
Turn off water at stop-valve	Run off water at tap
Unscrew cover	This lifts up (but not off) to expose the fixing-nut
Unscrew fixing-nut	Use a spanner and hold tap firmly so as not to loosen any pipe connections. If nut will not loosen easily, it will be necessary to wedge tap in position with a block of wood to take the strain from the pipe

What to do	*Main points to mention*
Remove upper part of tap	In most cold-water taps this is in two parts and the jumper is separate In hot-water taps and in some cold-water taps, the jumper is fixed in the spindle and is not separated. *See diagram*
Unscrew the nut which holds the washer, replace washer, and replace and tighten nut.	For *cold-water* use a *composition* or *leather washer*. For *hot-water* use a *rubber composition washer*
Replace jumper and upper part of tap	
Tighten fixing-nut tightly and screw down the cover	
Turn on water at stop-valve	Check that tap is working correctly

FIGURE 5.6

To prevent trouble, all taps should be inspected before cold weather as, if a dripping tap is left, the water will freeze in the waste pipes. In modern buildings it is becoming the practice to control each tap with a separate stopcock so that washers can be changed without disrupting the entire water supply; if this is not so, it is usual for a stopcock to control a section or wing of a building. The position of these stopcocks should be marked on the floor plans of the building for the guidance of the porter or handy-man.

The Worshipful Company of Plumbers was formed in 1365 but as yet there is no definite ruling on which side of the appliance the hot and cold taps should be placed.

WATER CLOSETS

These are of two types: the washdown and the siphonic (*see* Figure 5.7).

The *washdown* is the type in which the contents are removed by the force of the water flushed from the cistern or *water-waste preventer*. Efficiency depends on the head of water; high-level fittings were universal but now, with better design and when fitted correctly, low-level fittings are available and equally effective.

Siphonic closets clear the pan with a combined flushing and suction action. This is quieter than the washdown type and is considered to be more efficient but initially is more expensive to install. The cistern is usually of the low-level type.

Outwardly, both types look alike. Cistern flush is usually of 9·09 litres (2 gallons) of water but some authorities insist on 13·64 litres (3 gallons). This water must be discharged in 5 seconds.

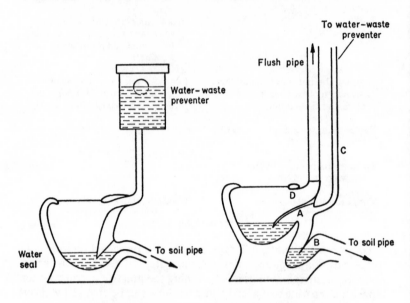

(a) Washdown W.C. pan   (b) Siphonic W.C. pan

FIGURE 5.7   Whasdown and siphonic water-closet pans
In the siphonic pan pipe *C* is connected to the flush pipe above the point shown. When the cistern is flushed, the force of the water sucks the air from pipe *C*. This creates a vacuum at *A* and the pressure forces the contents past *A* and *B* and into the soil-pipe. The seals are replaced by the after-flush.

Plastic seats are in common use and can be replaced readily at little cost; the other alternative is to have a polished wood seat. Where space is limited, the seats may have a cork top fitted so that they can also be used as a place to put towels or clothes.

The standard height for a W.C. is 406 mm (16 in.) plus the thickness of the seat but smaller heights can also be obtained which may be more convenient for children and older people.

CLEANING

The toilet is flushed and a lavatory cleaner is sprinkled in and left as long as possible. The pan is then brushed round with a lavatory brush and re-flushed, the brush being rinsed under the flow of clear water. Brown stains are removed with an abrasive and the brush; or, in bad cases, it may be necessary to mop out the water from the trap with a mop and bucket and rub hard with the abrasive. Salts of lemon may also be used.

The seat is wiped over daily with disinfectant and the outside and the flushing handle or pull wiped over with disinfectant or detergent and water. This is particularly necessary when there is any infection in the building.

URINALS

These are in the form of stalls or slabs with a continuous or intermittent flow of water. They must be fitted carefully as, if the jointing is faulty, water will leak beneath the slabs, and as it is not directly obvious can quickly lead to dry or wet rot.

Cleaning is similar to W.C.s but care must be taken with the sparge pipes or spreaders, particularly if they are copper, as an incrustation can build up on them which is difficult to remove.

W.C. CISTERN OR WATER-WASTE PREVENTERS

These are of two types (*see* Figure 5.8): the 'Burlington' which has a well-bottom and a siphonic action, and the 'piston' type which, when lifted, forces water over the top of the flush pipe. All cisterns have an overflow pipe through an external wall; any drip or running water from this indicates that the ball-valve controlling the inflow of water may be faulty and should be repaired.

SANITARY WARE

W.C.s, handbasins, and some baths, are made from either fireclay, earthenware, or vitreous china. The difference between them is:

Fireclay is a natural clay which is glazed and fired in one operation to give a hard dense material which is impervious to liquids and which cleans easily. As it is not possible to make articles as thinly as one can with earthenware or vitreous china it is used mainly for sinks and urinals.

Earthenware and *vitreous china* are made from a mixture of flint, china clay, ball clay, and china stone, with the quality depending on the percentage of the different ingredients and on the firing time. Vitreous china is cast thicker than earthenware and, as it contains more of the fusing agent, is a denser more glass-like material. Both are used for sanitary fittings, handbasins, and W.C. pans.

The main faults in this type of sanitaryware are crazing when fine cracks appear in the glaze. This can be caused by either underfiring, over-quick cooling, or when there is a different rate of shrinkage

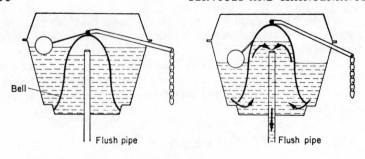

(a) Siphonic flushing cistern

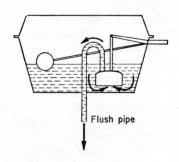

(b) Piston type cistern

FIGURE 5.8   W.C. cisterns

(a) When the chain is pulled, the bell is lifted. When released this forces water over the top of the flush pipe which drives the air from the pipe and forms a siphon which continues until the cistern is empty.

(b) Piston – when lifted, forces water over the top of the flush-pipe.

between the clay body and the glaze. Dunting is when a fine crack suddenly appears after the article has been in use for some time and is said to be caused by lack of control during the cooling process; it is *not* always caused by the dropping of a heavy object into the basin.

FITTINGS

Bathrooms and W.C.s should be clearly labelled. Now that there are so many foreign visitors in the country, there is much to be said for the practice of fixing explicit 'damen' and 'herren' symbols to the relevant doors; although, unfortunately, some of these can become collectors' pieces.

MIRRORS

These can be fixed above the handbasin or are adjustable with a swivel attachment. All should be well-lit with a built-in light just above.

RAZOR POINTS

Razor points are fitted close to the wash-basin and mirror. Attachments are available to fit an electric light socket but these are inadvisable for general use as either the wiring is pulled away from the lamp-holder or the shade becomes broken.

LAVATORY PAPER HOLDERS

These should be quick and easy to manipulate. Where rolls are used, there is a lot to be said for the outsize rolls and containers about 406 mm (16 in.) in diameter which are used on the Continent. They need less changing and are least likely to disappear when new.

LOCKS AND BOLTS

Lock and key are seldom used as keys easily become lost. Bolts should be secure. Where young children or elderly people are concerned the type of bolt which can be opened by a special key from the outside should be used (*see* Figure 5.9).

 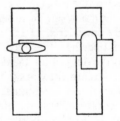

FIGURE 5.9   An indicator bolt
This can be opened from the outside by using a key on the centre spindle.

ELECTRICAL FITTINGS

Switches must not in any circumstances be fitted where they can be touched with wet hands so are either placed outside the bathroom, where they are switched on before entering, or else they are operated by a pull-cord from the ceiling. Electric heating, if used, must be fixed at a high level, and again operated by a pull-cord. Because of the danger, no portable electrical appliances should be used in the bathroom and no power sockets are fitted.

Bathroom units, complete with walls and all fittings and ready for connection to the water supply and drainage, are available. These are made from glass fibre or moulded plastic and prove very satisfactory when extra bathrooms are needed.

DRAINAGE AND SEWAGE

About two-thirds of the water supplied to a building has to be disposed of through the drainage and sewage systems; to achieve this the domestic drains are connected to a series of underground pipes or sewers which takes the waste to suitable points for discharge with or without treatment. It does not mean that the pipes can be smaller than those bringing water to the building. A 28 mm (1 in.) pipe delivers water at pressure and with some velocity but a 102 mm (4 in.) pipe is necessary to remove the waste as this flows through pipes which are only half to two-thirds full, at low speed, and always on a down-grade. Sewage must never flow under pressure as the effects of a burst pipe could be a menace to health and very unpleasant, moreover there is less chance of blockages when larger pipes are used. There is considerable leakage associated with sewer pipes, sometimes in a day this is as much as 2 820 litres/km (1 000 gal/mile), but the leakage is always from the outside into the pipe by ground water under pressure.

The average daily flow from domestic and industrial buildings plus ground water leakage is called the *dry weather flow* and is the basic figure in the design of sewers and treatment works. In Britain, this is usually considered at the rate of about 136 to 227 litres (30 to 50 gallons) per head per day.

It is the duty of the local authority to provide and maintain sewers and the treatment works. The drains on private property which run into the sewers are maintained by the occupier or owner. Any work on the drainage system, whether alterations or repairs, must be notified to the local authority which has the right to examine all drains and to insist on a proper means of drainage under the Public Health Acts.

The local authority may install a *combined system* of drainage in which surface water from the roofs and rainfall is carried in the same sewer as the soil and waste. This means that all the discharge has to be treated at the sewage works.

A *separate system* has two entirely different sets of drains, one for foul sewage and waste, and the other for the surface water and rainfall which, being unpolluted, can be discharged directly into streams, rivers, or the sea.

This separate flow system is more expensive to install but is preferred as *storm water overflows* are not required. In the combined system these can lead to pollution of streams and waterways by raw diluted sewage after there has been exceptionally heavy rain.

A *partially separate system* has two sets of sewers but some of the roof water flows into the foul sewer.

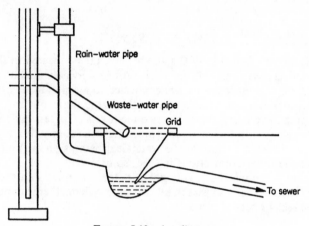

FIGURE 5.10   A gully trap

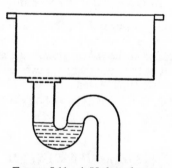

FIGURE 5.11   A U-shaped trap

To prevent the build-up of gases in the sewers and drains, these have to be ventilated. *Gully traps* (Figure 5.10) have also to be fitted to prevent the escape of these gases, and also rats and mice, from the sewers and drains into a building.

The most common type consists of a trap and a grated inlet; these should all be simple in construction and self-cleansing in action, and have a water-seal the depth of which depends on its position on the drainage system.

Any appliance, W.C., sink, or bath, connected to the drainage system has a similar U-shaped trap (Figure 5.11) to prevent the escape of gas into the building. In these the water-seal is usually 50 to 76 mm (2 to 3 in.) in depth.

Soil and waste water are removed from a building by one of three different systems: *a two-pipe system, a one-pipe system, or a single-pipe system.*

TWO-PIPE SYSTEM

In this, all soil fitments, W.C.s and urinals, are connected to the soil pipe and thence directly to the drain. All waste-water fitments, from baths, sinks, or handbasins, are connected to a separate set of waste pipes which are not connected directly to the drain but run into a gully trap. There are, therefore, two main sets of pipes, the soil and the waste pipes. But when there is more than one connection to a pipe there is always a danger of the water-seal being siphoned off when one of the other connections is used, so a second set of *anti-siphon* pipes has to be installed. This prevents the water-seals on the traps being siphoned off – so that in all two-pipe systems there are actually four stacks or sets of pipes.

ONE-PIPE SYSTEM

With this, all sanitary fittings, W.C., bath, and sink, are connected to the one pipe which is connected directly to the main drain.

Once again, because of the risk of siphonage, an extra anti-siphon pipe is fitted so that in this case there are two sets of pipes.

Whereas, in the two-pipe system, the waste-water seals are only 38 mm (1½ in.) deep, in the one-pipe system they are usually 76 mm (3 in.) deep.

SINGLE-PIPE SYSTEM

This is not permitted by all local authorities, but in some instances a single pipe may be fitted with no anti-siphon pipe.

A *fresh-air inlet* or air-vent is placed at the highest point of the drainage system. This is normally a continuation of the soil or waste pipe up to roof level; this pipe is left open with the top covered with a wire mesh to prevent blockage from twigs, leaves, or bird's nests.

Where the drains join or where the direction of the drain run alters, is placed an *inspection chamber*. The last inspection chamber on the property before the drain joins the main sewer is fixed at the lowest point of the house drain system. Some authorities expect an intercepting trap to be fitted at this point. When this is done, it is usual to ventilate the drainage system with a fresh-air inlet and ventilation

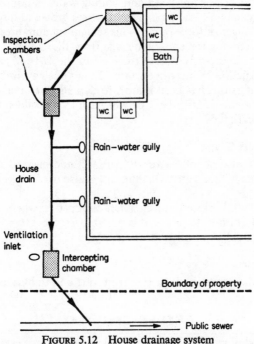

Inspection chambers

WC
WC
Bath
WC WC

Rain—water gully

House drain

Rain—water gully

Ventilation inlet

Intercepting chamber

Boundary of property

Public sewer

FIGURE 5.12   House drainage system

pipe. This should be about 914 mm (3 ft) above ground and should be kept free from overgrown hedges and bushes and all dirt and rubbish and face into the prevailing wind. *See* Figure 5.12.

In the past, the building bye-laws required all internal waste pipes to be taken directly out of a building by the shortest route; now, provided the local authority approves and the pipes and joints are acceptable to them, they may be inside the house; but an inside system costs more than one which is outside.

Generally, house drains may not be laid under a building; if this is done, they are enclosed in concrete and are made from specially approved iron. Where two buildings are joined so covering the drainage system, the local authority normally requires new drainage to be installed and the old system to be sealed off.

CLEANING AND MAINTENANCE

U-shaped traps

Those from sinks and handbasins can become blocked.
  To clear:
1. A handful of washing soda and boiling water is poured to flush, or completely fill, the pipe. This removes grease and scum.
2. Use a plunger or force pump. This sets up vacuum pressure in the pipe which may force any blockage from the U-bend.
3. Remove the cap-screw from the base of the U-bend and remove the obstruction by inserting a wire. Do not push a wire down from the basin as this has been known to damage the pipe.
4. If these methods fail, the pipe will have to be rodded back from the inspection chamber.

Outside Gully Traps

These are kept clear of leaves and rubbish and cleaned with a stiff brush, soda, and hot water. Disinfectant is also used, especially in hot weather.

If a building is closed during a hot summer or where the trap is connected to rain-water pipes, it is possible for the water-seals to dry up; they should be re-filled as necessary.

Fresh air inlets

Fresh air inlets must be kept free from dirt and unblocked.

REFUSE DISPOSAL

The disposal of refuse is always a problem in any large establishment. Rubbish is collected by the room-maids and is generally stored in disposable paper sacks on each floor, before being collected by a porter and taken to the main area for rubbish and to await collection by the local authority. In some establishments, refuse-chutes are incorporated in the building; rubbish is pushed into them and is dealt with by porters in the basement area.

A simpler method is to install a *waste-disposal unit* on each floor. The unit is fitted to a sink-unit and operates by refuse being cut or minced into small particles by a revolving blade and disposed of through the main drainage system. The system disposes of most refuse apart from metals, glass, and polythene.

A second method, which takes all refuse but requires a separate system of built-in pipework, is the Garchey system of waterborne refuse disposal (Figure 5.13). In this, all refuse, bottles, and cans are placed in a special receiver unit connected to a sink. By lifting a waste tube the refuse is flushed through the pipework to an underground collection chamber. At regular intervals, a collection tanker

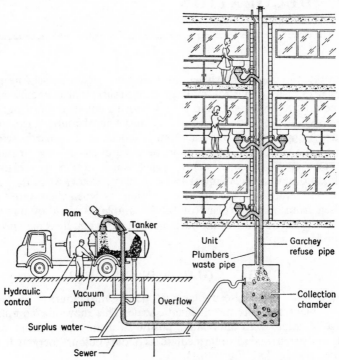

FIGURE 5.13 The Garchey system of waterborne refuse disposal

The householder simply puts refuse—food remnants, discarded oddments, bottles, and empty cans—into the special receiver unit connected to the sink. By lifting a waste tube the refuse is flushed through pipework to an underground collection chamber.

At weekly intervals a collection tanker vacuum-draws the waterborne refuse from the collection chamber. The surplus water is drained off and a mechanical ram inside the tanker compacts the contents into a semi-solid state.

The tanker contents are then disposed of by the Local Authority in their normal manner by tipping, burning, or treating.

vacuum-draws the waterborne refuse from the collection chamber. The surplus water is drained off and a mechanical ram inside the tanker compacts the contents into a semi-solid mass which is then disposed of by the local authority in the normal way.

6 COLOUR AND DECORATION

COLOUR is all important when considering any decorative scheme and goes a long way towards making an establishment attractive and welcoming to both guests and staff. Choosing colour is a fascinating exercise that can involve a lot of ingenuity and pleasure. It can also mean disappointment when a room is redecorated or partly refurnished and the colours chosen prove to be overpowering, or monotonous, or clash badly with a carpet which cannot be replaced. Colours do not always appear to be the same shade, when they are used on a wall or made up as curtaining, as when they were first chosen from a colour chart or fabric sample. Because of this the following brief outline of the variables of colour and light may prove helpful.

WHAT COLOUR IS COLOUR?

Red, orange, yellow, green, blue, and violet – the colours of the rainbow – blend to make the chromatic scale. This shows the complete range of colour with the relative positions of the pure colours, red, blue and green, and the intermediate secondary colours merging from one to another (*see* Figure 6.1).

When colour is combined it appears as white light. This is shown when a chromatic circle is spun rapidly or when a prism is used to split a ray of white light into its separate colours.

The differences between yellow and orange or red and blue are caused by the differences between the wavelengths of light.

Colour varies in three ways:

Hue

Hue which is the difference between one colour and another.

Tone or value

Tone or value which indicates the position in the light-to-dark scale.

Intensity or purity

Intensity or purity which indicates the amount of grey which has been added.

Neutral or achromatic colours

Neutral or achromatic colours are black and all the intermediate greys through to white; these can only vary in tone, not in hue or intensity.

Colours clash or become discordant when used in the same tone

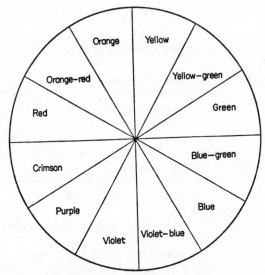

FIGURE 6.1   The colour circle

value; this can be avoided by using colour in the natural order of the colour circle but with the lighter hue always used in a lesser tone than that of the dark so that one colour is always dominant.

COLOUR SCHEMES

There are four main schemes favoured by designers.

1. Monochromatic

One colour is used in its different tones, such as a light, medium, and dark blue used with a background of a neutral colour. This scheme is often highlighted by the use of a little complementary colour either employed in cushions or perhaps in an outstanding painting.

2. Complementary

Any two colours from the opposite sides of the circle are used. These should never be of the same intensity – as a bright blue with a bright red – and they should always be used with a neutral colour and in unequal quantities so that one colour is allowed to dominate.

A refinement is *split-complementary* which uses a colour and one of the colours on either side of its complementary colour; this can give a very pleasing effect.

3. Harmonious or analogous

The colours chosen are close together and within the same quarter of the circle.

4. Triad

Colours are used from widely separated parts of the circle, again with a neutral background.

For a successful scheme, a good rule is that all the colours should have some connection with each other. The use of more than three or four colours should be avoided as this creates a 'bitty' effect with no focal point to which the eye is drawn.

All colour schemes are highly individual and must relate to the particular room and emphasize its main features and be suitable for the use to which it is going to be put. Decoration which is suitable and looks wonderful in one building may be completely wrong in another place as the proportions, aspect, and style of furnishings, may be completely different.

Bright reds, yellows, and orange are stimulating and gay and give a warm and friendly welcome if used in reception, entrance halls, and public rooms. Pastel colours are more restful and help to create a less dynamic effect; dark colours – provided that the lighting is suitable – give the impression of comfort and are used for a club or study atmosphere.

A room with a northern aspect will need the warmth given by the yellows, reds, and orange; whilst the cooler colours of blue, green, and grey, are more suitable for the sun.

Warm colours advance in a room and dominate more than the cool colours which recede. In this way, a room which is large and ill-proportioned can be made to look smaller by the use of dark warm colours on walls or ceiling, which will reduce the apparent width and height whilst a small room can be made to seem bigger by the use of light colours.

As was mentioned in a previous chapter, a change from dark colours to light, or vice versa, does affect the level of illumination so that, if there is a complete change of colour, this will also mean an alteration to the lighting to maintain the same standards.

Dullness is usually the result of a lack of contrast between light and shade or else a disparity of scale.

When decorating from the beginning with everything new, it is simplest to start by deciding the general atmosphere that is needed – such as brightness, restfulness, or a sense of opulence – and then to work on a colour scheme based on the largest area in the room, which is usually the carpeting. All other colours should tone or contrast with this.

Other schemes may be built around special furniture or a particular architectural feature of the room. Complete furnishing and decorating usually only happens when an establishment is newly opened and is often planned by consultant designers after long discussion on the purpose and impression to be created. Housekeepers and managers should be involved in these initial talks as they have the practical experience in the use, cleaning, and maintenance of the fabrics, colours, and materials which are recommended.

When re-decoration and re-furnishing take place, the Housekeeping Department frequently has full control. The task can often be difficult as it is seldom that everything is replaced at the same time, and new wall finishes or new curtainings have to blend with the existing furnishings and basic colour scheme. The problem is to achieve a harmonious effect which is different whilst making full use of partly-worn fabrics and furniture.

Rooms form a background for those using them and for this reason extremes in colour should be avoided unless the tastes of the users are well known. Many people will feel acutely uncomfortable if dressed in a colour which contrasts badly with the décor: a red or pink dress can look atrocious with a carefully worked out copper and orange colour scheme for a north-facing room.

For an amateur in the use of colour, the best way to develop good decorative skill is to see and study as many different schemes as possible, to select those which are most acceptable, and then try to analyse how the colour, texture, and fabrics have been used, how one colour dominates and emphasizes or hides any special feature, and how effective the result has been. Conversely, where a room is uninteresting and mediocre, try to decide why this is so and decide how you would set about remedying it, if you had such a room in your own establishment. Very good decorative schemes can be found in many of the better departmental furnishing stores designed to set off their stock to the best advantage.

The best of designs are usually extremely simple.

FACTORS WHICH AFFECT COLOUR

These include the following:

1. THE SOURCE OF LIGHT

The source of light whether natural or artificial. Building materials, fabrics, and paints absorb some of the bands of wavelengths of light and reflect the remainder. An extremely sunny day with a high level of illumination seems to bleach the colour out of materials, as only a certain percentage of the wavelengths can be absorbed and a greater amount of white light is reflected; conversely, colours appear darker and more intense on a dull day as more of the wavelengths of available light are absorbed. This explains why colour can alter so dramatically with the intensity and the quality of light, particularly when artificial light is used.

A filament tungsten lamp gives predominantly a yellow-orange-red light, so fabrics reflect colour in this warm yellow and red range and creams, buffs, and yellows become deeper; green hardly changes; but a blue will be greyer and have a greenish tendency; and, whilst the reds and oranges are more vivid, a purple may appear as a dull crimson.

Fluorescent light is chosen for the effect required; 'daylight' is good for most colours but makes blues more vivid and reds dull; 'warm' and 'white' will deepen most colours and make blues and greens greyer, and dull the pinks and reds. If colour match is important all fabrics, paints, and wall coverings must be seen in both daylight and in artificial light and, preferably, in the room and situation for which they are intended.

The degree to which colour is reflected is also important when considering choice, especially with shaded north-facing rooms or corridors with little direct light. Reflection factors are expressed as a percentage of the amount of light reflected from a pure white surface and values can be obtained for most paints and materials.

As an example, the reflection values for a glossy finish paint are:

Magnolia and jonquil	82%
Vanilla, silver, and the paler blues	72%
Lavender, canary yellow, and buff	65%
Sky blue, court grey, brass, and eau-de-nil ...	43%
Cherry, mid-green, and blue-grey	7%
and Black	$\frac{1}{2}$%

This leads to the principle of different coloured walls and ceilings; where there is strong excessive sunlight, one wall or ceiling painted in a dark colour absorbs the light and reduces the amount of glare and reflective light in the room. Most reflection is from the wall which is at right angles to the window and it is this wall which is normally a darker colour. The colour should, of course, be related to the decorative scheme of the room.

2. THE EYE OF THE BEHOLDER

A normally sighted person can see and differentiate between 100 and 160 colour hues and tones, but this ability varies considerably from one person to another. The difficulty is that there are two types of people who are colour defective: those who know that they are defective and those who do not. Colour blindness, which is an inherited defect, is the inability to distinguish reds and greens and is present in about 8% of the male population and about $\frac{1}{2}$% of the female. This is the extreme defect and in other cases the fault may only be apparent in certain tonal ranges. Colour defects may also develop with increasing age or through illness.

Colour sensations are transmitted by the cells of the eye retina. These cells are of two types; the rods which only see and transmit lightness and darkness, and the cones which receive the wavelengths for the three basic colours of red, green, and blue which combine together into the entire colour range.

If the eye is constantly looking at a strong basic colour, such as red or green, these receptor cones in the retina tire and lose their sensitivity and the opposite complementary colour is seen as an after-image. This is one reason why a complementary colour is used to balance strong dominant colours so as to ease eye-strain. A basic example of this comes from the hospital operating theatre where green is used for the doctors' and nurses' gowns and is a complementary colour to the red of blood.

3. THE COLOUR OF AN ARTICLE

The colour of an article alters in relation to the colours around it. A colour against a dark ground will appear much lighter than it does against a white or light background when it darkens, giving an apparent change of tone. A blue-green will appear bluer against a green background but greener on a blue ground.

Colour is very difficult to describe. What is a lime-green to one person can easily be said to be deep-yellow by another. Is lilac pink or blue? To overcome this difficulty there have been over the years varied attempts to classify colour and record the hue and the degree of grey in each. A complicated but very descriptive classification has been devised by an American, A. H. Munsell; based on this, in 1957, the Building Research Station compiled the British Standard 2660 Range of Colour which is intended primarily for the Painting and Decorating Trade but is a very useful method of identification.

The British Colour Council have also issued a Dictionary of Colours for Interior Decoration with each colour appearing in a matt and a gloss finish and as a carpet sample. The book is, however, expensive and is best seen at one of the local Colleges of Art.

A constant colour match for paints is possible but, as pigments and dyes vary when applied to different materials and textures, it is extremely difficult to match exactly different fabrics for curtainings and carpets. Even if the match is good in daylight, the effect with artificial lighting may be disastrous. If fabric and texture are different, a contrasting colour or one which is in harmony is usually used in decorative schemes.

7 WALL FINISHES AND CEILINGS

PERMEABLE AND IMPERMEABLE FINISHES

THE simplest of all wall finishes may be regarded by some people as no finish at all. As a means of introducing texture and muted colour into a room, there is an increasing tendency by architects to leave unplastered brickwork and timbers to provide the main decorative feature. This, with a stronger colour introduced by the curtaining or other fabrics, can create a very good functional impression for a modern establishment. It is a technique which has been used in a number of the newer university buildings and residences; that it also reduces or completely eliminates any maintenance costs may only be a secondary reason. Housekeeping problems can, however, become more difficult as the rougher surfaces hold dust, cobwebs, and dirt more readily.

The normal finish is to cover all bricks and mortar with plaster. This plaster and the bricks and timber used in the construction, have to dry out completely before they can be covered by any material or paint which is impervious to water. When completed an average sized house will contain about 6 800 litres (1 500 gallons) of water, and a large hotel or residence considerably more; this takes from six months to a year to dry out.

If moisture is sealed into the walls by a high gloss paint or a vinyl wall covering, both of which are impervious to water, the dampness will either lift, blister, or cause damp-marks on the paper, or blister the paint. In the drying out process, alkali salts may be brought to the surface causing efflorescence or crystalline growths; these pass through a permeable paint, the surface will lift, and the paint may discolour. In some cases, plaster may soften or a growth of mould may develop.

It follows from this gloomy picture that the final wall finish should be left until the drying process has been completed; unfortunately this is rarely possible as buildings are put to use as soon as they can be. Any finish that is used in this early stage in the life of a building must be permeable to allow the moisture to come to the surface and dry out. An impermeable finish, such as a high gloss oil paint or a vinyl wall-paper, should not be used.

TYPES OF PAINT AVAILABLE

ALKYD OR OIL-BASED

These are basically a mixture of pigments and a drying oil; this was originally a natural oil such as linseed, but is now usually a synthetic alkyd resin. These paints are made in three types of finish: gloss, eggshell, and flat. To thin, a solvent must be used.

A gloss finish is highly durable with good cracking and abrasive resistant properties. It stands up well to repeated washing and is most suitable for bathroom and kitchen conditions where there is high humidity, and for all exterior and interior work where a glossy durable finish is needed.

An eggshell finish does not have such a high sheen, is equally durable, and can be used for interior work and in kitchens and bathrooms, but it is not generally recommended for exterior work.

A flat finish is a washable interior paint which is used for all wall and ceiling surfaces but is not suitable for kitchen or bathroom work where high humidity or dirt conditions occur. The paint can be washed but not to the extent of, or as frequently as, a gloss or eggshell finish.

To extend the life of these alkyd paints other synthetic materials such as polyurethane, are now being built-in by the manufacturers. This type of paint should not be used on new plaster.

EMULSION

These paints are water-based and are an emulsion of a polymer, polyvinyl acetate, alkyd, and styrene-butadiene, which is closely related to the synthetic resins. The main advantages are that water is used as a thinner and, as the paint is permeable, it can be used with new plastering. Durability is good, the paint washes well, and it can be used for all interior and exterior building surfaces, including kitchens and bathrooms, where a semi-glossy durable finish is needed.

WATERPAINTS AND DISTEMPERS

Waterpaints and distempers have been largely replaced by the emulsion paints. They are unsuitable for exterior work or where there is high condensation or humidity, as in kitchens and bathrooms. They are not as durable as the other paints and will not stand up to any regular washing routine.

CELLULOSE

The main difference between a cellulose paint and oil paints is that drying is brought about entirely by the evaporation of the solvent base. These cellulose paints are extremely hard-wearing finishes which are usually sprayed on, as the drying is usually too rapid for the paint to be applied by brush. As the paint film is so hard, it is unsuitable to apply to any surface or soft woods which are liable to expand or contract. These paints are generally multi-coloured and are very good as a mask to surface defects.

HEAT-RESISTING PAINTS

Advice should be taken from the manufacturers concerning this type of paint, particularly when light colours are required. Generally, a fluctuation in temperature puts more strain on the paint film than does a lengthy exposure to a steady temperature.

APPLYING PAINT

1. All surfaces must be clean and grease-free.
2. Cracks must be filled, woodwork must be rubbed down with glass-paper, then pumice stone, to provide a key for the new paint. If the previous paint is in poor condition it should be stripped or burned off.
3. New wood always requires a primer; whether plaster requires priming depends on the final finish.
4. Specifications usually require either two coats of undercoat and one of the final finish or else one coat of undercoat and two of the final finish, with no consecutive coats being of the same shade, except in the case of white.
5. Each coat of paint should harden before the next is applied. If this is not done, or if the paint dries too quickly, it will have no time to sink into the surface and hold, and the final coat may develop a network of tiny cracks because the under-surface has not been ready.
6. No painting should be done under adverse weather conditions. Paints should not be applied if the temperature falls below 4·4° C (40° F) as they become difficult to use, drying is slowed, and the appearance may be affected. Conversely, very hot conditions will thin the paint so that the film is excessively thin; this will increase the speed of drying so that brush marks are evident. High humidity, fog, or rain may cause drying problems and tackiness, and also affect the finished appearance.

NOTES ON CLEANING PAINTWORK, WALLS, AND CEILINGS

1. Dust should be removed with either a duster or a light impregnated mop or by suction cleaner. Do not rub the dust into the surface.
2. Wash using a netcloth or sponge, water, and detergent, and rinse with clear water. If the paint is particularly dirty and ingrained, a fine abrasive can be used but this may damage the surface and its use should be avoided as much as possible.
3. When washing a really dirty surface start at the bottom and work upwards. This prevents trickles of water running down the wall and marking. These marks can be very difficult to remove when the lower part of the wall is washed; so, start at the bottom.
4. Ceilings can be washed in the same way as walls using a sponge, but the work is extremely tiring and is not recommended for normal cleaning staff. More usually, contractors or decorators will be brought in to do this.

   This will also apply when high walls are cleaned; adequate stepladders and safety measures must be employed. It may be the policy of the firm or of the Trade Union concerned that cleaning will not be undertaken by female domestic staff beyond a certain height. Where there is no such policy, a common-sense attitude should be adopted and the work done by the younger more agile members of staff.

WALL-PAPERS

As a wall finish these offer considerable scope and variety of colour, texture, pattern, finish, and price; and provide an effective and quick method of altering the whole concept of a room. Papers vary from the basic surface print, to oatmeal papers where texture is introduced by the addition of chopped straw or wood-dust, to grass papers with woven grass or fibres mounted on a paper base, to those with an embossed (or anaglypta) finish. Flock papers are those papers coated with an adhesive to which the flock – of silk, cotton, or man-made fibres – is stuck to give a raised pattern. Papers are produced which realistically imitate stonework, polished woods and veneers, embroideries and tapestries, or have a glinting metallic print.

Patterns can be large or small but should be chosen in relation to the room dimensions and the result to be achieved. A horizontal pattern gives added width whilst a vertical pattern adds height to a room. Large patterns will make a room appear smaller; a small pattern enlarges. As has been mentioned elsewhere, too many different colours in a room gives an effect of 'bittiness', and too many diffierent patterns tend to fight each other unless they are very dissimilar and contrasting.

Where there is hard wear or where paper can get splashed in cloakrooms or bedrooms, it is an advantage to use either smearproof or washable paper, which has a coating of transparent synthetic resin.

All papers damage easily. Protection is given by using glass or perspex at entrances, around light switches, by wash-handbasins, and wherever damage is likely to occur. Narrow strips of wood fixed 50 to 75 mm (2 to 3 in.) from the wall help to prevent chairs and other furniture being pushed against the wall. Stronger material, such as vinyl fabric, formica, or wood panelling, is used to protect either as a dado on the lower part of the wall or else as a surround to a bed-head or back of a divan section where wear can be expected from occupants leaning back against the wall.

Wall-papers can be repaired by the careful matching of spare paper or by sticking torn parts into place. Grease can occasionally be removed with a grease absorbent such as Fuller's earth or, in an emergency, talc powder; how successful this is depends on the type of paper and the type of grease. If parts of the wall are vulnerable and cannot be protected, odd left-over lengths of paper should be kept for renovations.

CLEANING

Embossed or deeply textured papers collect and hold considerably more dust than a smooth paper. All papers are dusted with a clean wall brush or suction cleaner. If the paper is washable, marks are removed by light sponging, otherwise by rubbing with a little soft bread or indiarubber.

QUANTITIES REQUIRED

When *calculating* the *amount of paper* which is *needed* the 'drop' or pattern repeat measurements must be taken into account as paper must match when hung. A large pattern will mean an extra allowance added to the measurement and increase the costs for decoration.

Paper is sold in rolls which are 0·54 m (21 in.) wide and 10 m (33 ft) long to give a surface area of 5·4 m² (57·5 ft²). This, divided into the area of the wall surface to be covered, will give the number of rolls required.

For example: if the perimeter of a room is 25·6 m (84 ft) and the height is 3 m (10 ft) the area will be 76·8 m² (840 ft²) and the number of rolls of paper required would be:

$$\frac{76\cdot8}{5\cdot4} = 14+ \quad or \quad \left(\frac{840}{57\cdot5} = 14+ \right)$$

As it is not possible to buy a fraction of a roll, 15 rolls of wallpaper would be bought.

For all good class work, lining paper, applied horizontally around the room, is used under the top paper.

Ceiling papers, both textured and flat, are often used to hide poor surfaces, and to give a decorative effect. When re-decorating, these are not removed but painted over.

OTHER FINISHES

Paint and wall-paper are both wall finishes which are cheap and easy to apply, but do not have an indefinite life and are usually renewed every five to seven years. Other wall coverings are more durable – and often initially more expensive – and are used where a more permanent decorative treatment is required or where expense is no barrier.

Vinyl Wall Coverings

Vinyl Wall Coverings are very durable with good stain resistance, are easy to clean and, if necessary, to scrub, and are produced in a wide variety of colour, texture, and design; *but* as they are impermeable to moisture, they cannot be used where there is any dampness.

Vinyl Surfaced Hardboard

Vinyl Surfaced Hardboard again is very hard-wearing, made in wood-grain or textured.

Laminated Plastics

Laminated Plastics are very suitable for bathrooms and cloakrooms.

Wood

Wood is used as panelling for walls and ceilings or as slats with a curtain or material backing.

Glass

Glass is used in the form of bricks or as patterned panels or screens and particularly in inner corridors, dark rooms, and basement areas, where the extra translucent light is needed.

Coloured glass panelling or tiles which are obtainable in many brilliant colours, are very hygienic and easy to clean and are of great use for bathrooms and as a protection behind wash-handbasins or other vulnerable places.

Mirror glass is used as a means of introducing extra light into dark areas and alcoves and to give the impression of greater space.

Marble, Mosaics, and Ceramic Tiles

Marble, Mosaics, and Ceramic Tiles are used in various shapes and patterns.

Curtains

Curtains make a quick and easily changed decoration and are a means of hiding bad or irregular walls whilst giving a soft effect and the impression that windows or further rooms are beyond.

Woven Materials

Woven Materials, used either as panels or paper backed, are effective and can match the other furnishings. The fabrics most commonly used are grass and silk-cloths, linens, jute, rayons, some of the rougher tweeds, leather, and some of the cheaper range of floor coverings such as carpeting, cork tiles, linoleum, and vinyl sheeting. All are hard-wearing and, if used with discretion, have their place.

The main consideration when assessing a wall finish is to decide how often the décor is to be changed and to buy accordingly.

CEILINGS

These are usually finished in paint, ceiling papers, or with acoustic tiles to reduce noise, but many of the other types of wall coverings can be adapted for ceiling use.

An old building with high rooms is frequently modernized by reducing the apparent height and installing a false ceiling. This may be made from acoustic tiles but also from covered panels or by fitting wooden or metal slats.

8 FLOORINGS AND FLOOR COVERINGS

IN THE introduction to a paper issued by the Building Research Station on 'The resistance to wear of flooring materials' is the statement that a floor 'is seldom expected to last for less than ten years and often has to last for more than twenty years'. Many firms would expect the twenty-year period to be extended or even doubled before new flooring is required.

All floorings should be carefully chosen as not all are suitable for every purpose; all have advantages and disadvantages.

Flooring is chosen for its wearing qualities and for appearance, but all are dependent on the condition and evenness of the sub-floor beneath it.

SUB-FLOORS

A good, level, damp-proof sub-floor has a considerable effect on the 'life' of the floor laid above it and it is important that an uneven or damp sub-floor is made good before the final finish is applied.

Many materials, tiles, P.V.C., linoleum, and thermo-plastics, are stuck directly to the sub-floor and as it is difficult to get an adhesive which is completely resistant to damp, any damp must first be treated either by using a damp-proof membrane or by laying a topping screed of asphalt. This must be approximately 16 mm (5/8th in.) thick and it will of course also provide a smooth and level surface. Another alternative is a sand and concrete screed but a new concrete floor, even with a damp-proof membrane, should be left uncovered for at least twelve weeks so that it can dry out completely.

In the older type buildings suspended wooden floors are often found and these are frequently uneven as moisture absorption or excess drying-out will cause movement in the wood and a consequent swelling or warping. Being made mainly of softwoods these floors also wear unevenly leaving protruding knots and blemishes. When this happens an old floor can be renovated by planing or sanding or it may be covered with sheets of hardboard or plywood. This gives a sufficiently smooth surface for most types of floor, with the exception of some of the very flexible covers, such as cork and rubber. When these are used, the jointing between all the boards *must* be tight or filled as any slight irregularity will quickly show through on the upper surface. It may even be necessary to insert an under-layer of felt paper to ensure absolute smoothness.

In an older building it is hardly necessary to say that it is advisable to check that the floor will *not* have to be taken up at some future date for re-wiring or re-plumbing purposes.

FACTORS AFFECTING THE CHOICE OF FLOORING

1. *COST*

This varies greatly from one type of flooring to another but, in addition to the initial cost and the cost of laying, which includes adhesives and labour, and the expense involved in the preparation or repair of the sub-floor, consideration must be given to the cost of maintenance each year. The King Edward's Hospital Fund for London in their report on 'Floor Maintenance in Hospital Wards' have done an interesting survey on the comparative costs of different flooring materials. In their particular investigation, they calculated that the annual labour costs to maintain $92 \cdot 9$ m^2 (1 000 ft^2) of corridor ranged from £34 to £61 a year. Their survey was on vinyl asbestos, P.V.C. sheeting and tiles, linoleum, cork, rubber, and composition floors, and was also concerned with the durability of each material and methods of cleaning.

The true cost of a floor will include the initial cost, the laying charges, and the estimated cost of maintenance each year; it should also take into account the expected life of the floor.

2. *APPEARANCE*

This is of major importance as the floor is the largest single area and affects the appearance of everything else in the room. Colour should be of a shade and tone which will blend with the existing and future decorative schemes. A very light or very dark floor surface shows dust and marks quickly whilst a patterned or marbled surface makes them less noticeable.

3. *DURABILITY AND QUALITY*

These two points are closely related. Most coverings are sold in differing grades of thickness depending on their area of use, whether for heavy duty or for light traffic areas. A bedroom or a rarely used top-floor corridor will not require the same grade of P.V.C. or carpeting that is required in the main entrance hall or public lounge. The grade bought *must* be suitable for the use and wear it will have; but, if for prestige reasons it is the policy to change regularly the décor, it is sensible to buy a lower grade carpet or flooring with an estimated life from one re-decoration to the next. This mainly applies to hotels and those places which trade on their prestige and appearance and does not apply to most other establishments where the flooring is required to last for as long as possible.

Also to be considered is the floor's resistance to stains, indentation from furniture and heels, mildew risk, and the resistance to burns and heat. This latter point can be easily tested by stubbing out a cigarette end or matches on sample pieces of the floor to see how it reacts to this type of burn or the ease with which it ignites; one finds, in this way, that some floorings which otherwise seemed suitable can be a fire hazard.

The floor should be stable and not prone to shrinkage or unusual stretching, nor easily chipped or cracked, nor lose its colour.

4. COMFORT

The questions to be asked here are: is it hard to walk on, is it 'warm or cold', is it a quiet floor, is it suitable for the use to which the room will be put?

Quietness would be particularly considered in corridors which are outside lecture rooms, conference rooms, libraries, in nurses' homes, and all residences where people are coming and going and sleeping at odd hours.

5. SAFETY

The floor should have non-slip qualities when both dry and wet; as the greatest number of accidents occur through falling there seems no point in adding to the statistics.

As yet, there is no flooring which answers all the requirements.

TYPES OF FLOORINGS

WOOD

For many years, wood has been the traditional method of flooring. *Softwoods*, such as pine, fir, or spruce – deal boards – are mainly used for floor-boarding which is then covered by linoleum, P.V.C., or carpeting.

Hardwoods have a longer life and wear more evenly than the softwoods having finer fibres to give a much smoother surface which is comparatively free from knots. Because of this and their appearance and the wide variety of colour in which they are obtainable, hardwoods are more likely to be left uncovered as strips, wood block, or parquet flooring. Initial cost is higher but they have a long life expectancy and costs can be reduced by saving on further floor covering.

There is a large (and confusing) selection of hardwoods available. Originally oak, beech, and occasionally elm, were used but now many hardwoods are imported from overseas: these include teak, Australian jarrah, East African olive, abura, guarea, and mansonia. All these timbers have differing degrees of hardness, resilience, resistance to indentation, and colour, and one needs to consult an expert before a final decision is made as to which is the most suitable wood for a particular area.

To confuse the issue, some hardwoods are softer than some of the softwoods, some of the cheaper hardwoods being used in place of softwoods as floor-boarding. Generally, hardwoods are obtained from deciduous trees.

All woods must be well seasoned and kiln-dried before use, and some public authorities stipulate that flooring timber is air-dried for at least one year before kiln-drying. The moisture content should be from 10 to 12% where there is central heating, and from 14 to 16% where there is none; if the water content increases to over 20% unprotected wood is liable to attack from dry or wet rot. Because of this, all timber floors must be well ventilated having a free passage of air over at least one surface. This means that a wooden floor laid directly on a damp-proofed concrete base will remain sound provided it is not then covered by tiling or carpeting which restricts the ventilation. Conversely, a suspended wood floor covered with P.V.C. or linoleum is ventilated from below by the airbricks which are built into the house construction and which must be kept free from blockage by dirt or leaves. Trouble can also be caused when the humidity of a building is suddenly reduced, as when central heating is installed, as then floors and furniture dry, becoming brittle, and cracks may develop. It should be noted that all woods are not suitable for the installation of under-floor heating.

Traditionally, hardwood block and strip floors are 25 mm (1 in.) in thickness, but during the last few years many floors have been laid which are only 9·5 mm ($\frac{3}{8}$ in.) thick.

Hardwood Strip Flooring

Hardwood Strip Flooring is 25 × 76 mm (1 × 3 in.) and of varying lengths. These strips are tongued and grooved at both sides and the ends and are nailed to an understructure. This may be joists or laths of wood let into a concrete sub-floor or a softwood sub-floor.

Wood Blocks

Wood Blocks are usually 25 × 76 × 229 mm (1 × 3 × 9 in.), interlocked by tongue and groove joints and stuck directly on to a cement and sand screed.

Parquet

Parquet is a general description applied to a thin hardboard overlay, glued and pinned over an existing softwood floor which has to be completely even. Both wood block and parquet are laid in many different patterns.

Composition Wood Blocks

Composition Wood Blocks are made from a mixture of wood, cement, gypsum, calcium carbonate, colourings, and linseed oil; this is compressed and left to cure for some months. They have the advantage of looking similar to a hardwood block but are cheaper, more fire-resistant, do not suffer from either expansion or contraction, and so are of particular use where under-floor heating is concerned.

Treatment

All woods should be protected either by paint, varnish, or preservative and, in the case of floors, by a seal and polish. Water should be used sparingly or not at all. The old traditional policy of a well-scrubbed floor may have been good for the soul but certainly was not good for the floor.

Over the past few years, experiments have been going on in this country and in America into the impregnation of the wood cells with a (plastic) vinyl monomer which sets within the wood to give a solid plastic material fixed within the wood structure. The advantage is that the wood is very stable and will not shrink or swell, is much harder and tougher and easier to maintain than untreated wood, and is also resistant to attack from fungi and insects.

Most wooden floors can be resurfaced by sanding if they become rough or show signs of wear.

MASTIC ASPHALT AND PITCHMASTIC

These floorings are of asphalt, bitumen, or coal-tar pitch, which is used as a binder with a mineral filler such as powdered granite. It is laid and spread *in situ* when it is hot resulting in a smooth crack-free finish. The British Standards and Building Centre Code of Practice say that 'mastic asphalt flooring laid in accordance with the recommendations of the code is dustless, odourless, jointless, and impervious to the transmission of moisture either in liquid or vapour form'.

It is also durable and flame and rat-proof, and will withstand most temperatures normally encountered. It is, however, unsuitable for kitchen use as grease, fats, oils, paraffin and turpentine can cause considerable damage to the surface and must be wiped off immediately.

Special grades have been developed as water-proof sub-floors for linoleum, rubber, wood blocks, or other finishes. These sub-floors are laid in one layer 16 mm ($\frac{5}{8}$ in.) thick.

Treatment

When they are newly laid, they should be left for at least one week to harden properly. Superficial dirt is mopped off or the floor is scrubbed with detergent and water, rinsed, and allowed to dry. All grease, fats, and oils should be removed at once.

THERMOPLASTIC TILES

These are made by heating and grinding together a mixture of short-fibre asbestos, powdered mineral fillers, thermoplastic binders, fluxes, and pigments. The hot mixture is passed through heated rollers and then cut into tiles. These are usually 229×229 mm (9×9 in.) and vary in thickness from 2·0 mm to 3·2 mm. Cost is related to grade and to the colour, the darker tiles being cheaper than the brighter colours.

Their great advantage is that, provided that there is no water pressure from below, they can be laid on solid concrete which has no damp course. Apart from a very slight expansion, thermoplastic is unaffected by water and, instead of acting as a damp-proof barrier, will allow moisture to penetrate to the surface.

The tiles are non-slip and fairly resilient but they can be noisy and will show indentations quickly and any unevenness through from the sub-floor. At ordinary temperatures the tiles are brittle but when laid on a flat rigid base they are reasonably durable although they can crack under weight or with movement of the sub-floor. They will also soften with heat.

The ordinary type of thermoplastic is not resistant to oil or grease but special grades are available which have greater resistance and can be used in kitchens.

Treatment

The floor is wet-mopped or scrubbed with detergent and water, rinsed, and dried. It can be polished with a water-based emulsion wax and can be sealed, but a spirit or paraffin-based cleaner should not be used as this will soften and break up the surface.

CORK

Cork can be obtained in sheet or tile form and is made from granulated cork bark which is compressed at a high temperature when the natural resins in the cork bind the granules together. No additional binder is needed. The colour ranges from a light honey to darker walnut shades or it can be pigmented to a soft green.

Cork must never be laid on an unventilated wooden sub-floor as the normal movement of the wood may break the cork surface. The sub-floor must be very smooth and should be sanded or covered with hardboard or plywood (and, if necessary, felt paper) before laying, so that there are no irregularities to show through which will ridge the cork.

Cork is very resilient and soft underfoot and extremely quiet; but, because it is so soft and porous, unless it is carefully maintained it is neither hardwearing nor durable, as dirt, grit, and stains become embedded in the surface. All cork floors should be sealed as soon as they are laid.

Thickness ranges from 6·5 mm ($\frac{1}{4}$ in.) to a heavy duty thickness of 12·7 mm ($\frac{1}{2}$ in.). An extra heavy tile with a high density has a weight of 16·4 kilos: 0·06 m³ (36 lb: ft³).

Cork is very suitable for libraries, churches, schools, and places where quietness is of first importance but is usually used only in areas where traffic is light.

Treatment

For ease of maintenance, these floors should be sealed as soon as they are laid and further protection given by regular polishing. Daily cleaning consists of sweeping with an impregnated mop; heavier dirt can be removed by damp-mopping with a neutral detergent. The floor should be kept as dry as possible.

Where these floors have not been sealed, dirt is best removed by spray cleaning/polishing with the dirt being taken up into the nylon or metal-fibre pads. The floor is then buffed.

When there has been heavy wear, the floor may be resurfaced by sanding; this is a specialist job but puts many added years on to the life of the floor.

Some cork flooring is now being manufactured with a 0·5 mm surface layer of vinyl; this gives greater durability whilst retaining all the advantages of cork.

When exposed to sunlight, many corks tend to fade, which leads to a patchy effect if rugs or furniture are moved about the room.

Provided the temperature does not exceed 26·7° C (80° F), cork is suitable for under-floor heating.

POLYVINYL CHLORIDE

Polyvinyl Chloride (P.V.C.) is a harmless looking white powder which, when mixed with other ingredients, plasticizers, fillers, and pigments, and subjected to heat and pressure can be changed into many different types of material. It can be tough, hard, or resilient, or be made into a fabric which is soft and elastic. It was first discovered in 1838 but was not used commercially until the 1930s, and it has only taken the major share of the market in floorings since the early 1950s.

P.V.C. is a very flexible and durable floor which can be produced in tile or sheet form usually 2·0 mm or 2·5 mm in thickness.

Printed vinyl sheet is produced in a vast variety of pattern and texture to reproduce the effect of natural stone, ceramic tile, or wood veneer; colours can be bright and clear. A foaming technique produces a P.V.C. which is softer to the tread than an ordinary vinyl; a three-dimensional effect can also be produced by floating flakes of P.V.C. in a clear vinyl base.

P.V.C. is resistant to indentation, stains, oils, and grease; it is softened by any solvent or spirit so that only water-based polishes or seals can be used. Some vinyls are affected by heat over 26.7°C (80°F); some, but not all, are badly affected by cigarette burns and should be tested for this before buying.

P.V.C. can be laid on any type of sub-floor; but, as it is impervious to water, any rising damp or moisture will weaken the adhesive and cause it to loosen or blisters to appear under the tiles or sheeting. Blisters are caused by the expansion of the moisture due to heat; the minimum of water should be used when cleaning if the P.V.C. is laid in tile form.

Sheet vinyl has the advantage of being laid with the joins or seams heat-welded to give a finished joint-free surface and thus, with the edges coved at wall and corners to prevent cracks and crevices, is of particular use in hospitals, nursing homes, or sick quarters where hygiene is of importance.

For a quieter and more resilient flooring, some P.V.C.s now have a felt or sponge rubber backing.

Treatment

P.V.C. can be sealed depending on the amount of traffic and wear, but it is debatable whether there is any particular advantage in doing so.

It is swept with an impregnated dry mop, can be wet-mopped when needed, and is usually polished to maintain its gloss. Black scuff marks may have to be removed by rubbing with a little fine wire wool and liquid polish.

An interesting development is the technique of building fluorescence into the vinyl which makes the whole floor glow when used with ultra-violet light; of great use in hospitals, it means that while patients are undisturbed by bright lights the staff can still move about easily. Other applications of this are for the illumination of stairs and corridors and in courtyards or out-of-doors as a wall covering or decorative pattern.

VINYL ASBESTOS

The introduction of asbestos fibre to the polyvinyl gives a more durable tougher substance and has the advantage of making the P.V.C. resistant to solvents, mild alkalis, oils, and grease. Further advantages are that it does not burn as easily as P.V.C. and does not need a water-proof membrane under it. As yet, however, the seams cannot be welded. It should be noted that all vinyl flooring becomes extremely slippery when wet.

With all these 'solid' floorings the advantages and disadvantages of laying in sheet or tile form have to be considered. When laid in tile form the floor is easy to repair as a tile can be either renewed or stuck back in place; the disadvantage is that these tiles frequently loosen and often need attention. When tiles are well-laid the jointing should be sufficiently tight to prevent dirt lodging between the cracks. Tiles, in varied colours, often play a major part in the decorative scheme.

Sheeting is laid either with the minimum of joins or it can be welded into a seamless floor; but repair may be difficult needing either the replacement of a whole section or the insertion of a patch. The P.V.C. can be shaped and used as skirtings coved to make cleaning easier.

RUBBER

This is produced from natural or synthetic rubber in sheet or tile form and is obtainable in a wide range of colours. Rubber is very resilient, quiet, and soft under-foot, but it can in time be damaged by indentation and abrasion, as when it is laid under a revolving door. Oils, fats, and grease can damage the surface, as will any spirit or solvent-based polish which softens the rubber.

Cuts can be caused by sharp-edged furniture and stiletto and metal-tipped heels, but these cuts seem to heal together and are normally not noticeable. When dry, rubber has quite good non-slip properties but it can be dangerously slippery when wet and has been likened to an ice-skating rink.

It can be bonded to a sponge rubber backing to give a softer cushion effect. With age rubber tends to harden and may develop a craze of surface cracks.

Treatment

Sweep with an impregnated mop (not oil) and damp-mop with a neutral solution, or the floor can be polished and buffed, or a dry-bright polish can be applied.

LINOLEUM

Linoleum is made from a mixture of fine powdered cork, linseed oil, wood flour, colouring, and resin, blended together and backed by a hessian canvas or compressed felt. Grades vary from 3·0 mm to a thickness 6·7 mm which is used in the heaviest of traffic areas. The colour range is good in plain, marble, or patterned design. It is a very versatile traditional flooring which can be obtained in sheet or tile form.

Contrary to popular belief, linoleum should *not* be scrubbed and, if washing is necessary, the floor should be damp mopped only using little water and a neutral detergent. Alkalis or soda added to the water will remove the natural oil and eventually make the linoleum brittle and crumble; if it is wet, linoleum will expand; if it is left and kept wet, it will mildew and rot.

Linoleum can be laid directly on the sub-floor using an adhesive or it can be laid loose. When it is laid loose, the linoleum expands owing to absorption of moisture from the air; this means that it must be left for several weeks for the expansion to take place, then cut back to fit correctly. In this interim expansion period, the edges are protected by adhesive tape which covers the overlapping edges. When linoleum is stuck directly to the sub-floor, this expansion does not take place as movement is prevented by the adhesive.

With proper care and provided the right grade is bought, linoleum is a very durable flooring; it can show indentation but new types of linoleum are being developed which are highly resistant to this and other marking.

Treatment

Linoleum can now be bought either sealed or unsealed. If it is unsealed, the top dressing has to be removed before a seal can be applied.

To clean, the floor is swept with an impregnated mop or damp-mop using a neutral detergent and as little water as possible. Polish or spray clean, preferably with non-slip materials. Abrasives should be avoided as they damage the surface; marks can be removed with a little white spirit or paraffin.

Many linoleums have stood the test of time and are still in good condition after 40 or 50 years use. It remains to be seen how they will compare with the P.V.C.s and vinyl asbestos after the same period.

It should be mentioned here that many of these manufactured floorings include other ingredients and are becoming very similar as manufacturers look for better and better products. Some linoleums have an addition of P.V.C. and it is increasingly difficult to look at a floor and be able to say 'Yes, that is linoleum, rubber, or vinyl asbestos' with any certainty. One guide is often the temperature of the floor as some materials are much colder than others, but this comes with experience; there are good grounds for keeping some record or sample of a new floor in the Housekeeper's office for reference purposes.

QUARRY TILES AND CERAMIC TILES

Tiles, because of their hard-wearing qualities, have long been used in the service areas, kitchens, stores, and back corridors, where heavy wear is expected both from staff and from the movement of stores and equipment.

Quarry Tiles

Quarry Tiles are very strong and will stand up to most weights and impact without cracking or chipping. Resistance to heat, stains, indentation, oils, grease, alkalis, and acids, is good. When tiles are laid properly with tight seams, the floor is very hygienic and easy to clean. It is, however, cold and noisy and can become very hard if staff are on their feet all day. It can be slippery when wet but this can be obviated by using tiles with a slightly roughened or ridged surface. A quarry tile should have a hard-glazed surface to make it impervious to water.

Sizes vary from 101 mm, 152mm, to 229 mm (4, 6, to 9 in.) square with thickness depending on the grade and expected wear. To make cleaning easier, coved tiles for edges and corners are used and pre-cast slabs are fitted above service pipes and in cleaning gullies.

Ceramic Tiles

Ceramic Tiles are made from a finer quality of clay and are more colourful although not as tough as a quarry tile. They are very suitable for bathrooms, or cloakrooms and are occasionally found in public halls and entrances.

Treatment

Sweep with an untreated or impregnated brush or mop. Damp-mop using a neutral detergent or machine- or hand-scrub using a deck-scrubber.

Tessellated Tiles

Tessellated Tiles are very much smaller tiles often used as a mosaic.

MARBLE AND STONE

Marble and Stone provide one of the more permanent floorings which are attractive and easy to maintain. They are very durable but hard, cold, and noisy and initially expensive to install.

Amongst the more expensive marbles are Swedish green which can be light or dark coloured, and Bleu Belge which has whitish veins and is more black than blue and is often used in conjunction with Sicilian marble. Rose Aurora is pink with varying patches of white; Perlato, a deep cream with darker markings; Old Church Green and Serpintino give a range of greens.

The most usual sizes for marble tiles are 305×102 mm (12×4 in.) and 305×305 mm (12×12 in.). Thickness varies but can be as little as 9·5mm ($\frac{3}{8}$ in.). Pattern is varied.

Amongst the most common stone in use is Norwegian quarzite, or Alta quarzite, and Kotah stone from India. These polish and are very tough with a good resistence to stains, oils, and acids.

Treatment

Sweep with impregnated mop. Damp-mop with either plain water or a neutral detergent. Soap should not be used as this will make a marble very slippery. A *fine* abrasive may be used if needed.

A Granolithic Floor

A Granolithic Floor is a mixture of granite chippings set into a cement base to make a good heavy-duty floor for stores, cloakrooms, and kitchens. It is laid directly on a solid sub-floor with covings and pre-cast slabs to cover drainage gullies as required.

Treatment

Sweep with an impregnated dry mop, damp-mop using a neutral detergent, or machine-scrub.

This floor may dust, in which case the granolithic can be sealed and polished.

Terrazzo

Terrazzo is similar to a granolithic floor but marble chippings are used, instead of the granite. These are set in a finer cement base which may be coloured. Where there is a large floor area, the material is laid in sections which are separated by metal strips, or it can be laid in slab form. A smooth finish is given by machine grounding. This gives a hard, durable floor; to prevent staining, a seal is normally used followed by polish, although this is not always necessary, as a good gloss can often be produced by machine-buffing with no polish involved.

Treatment

As above and as for marble; if the terrazzo is old or really dirty an abrasive can also be used.

FLOOR SEALS AND POLISHES

As has been mentioned, to get the best wear from a floor, it is necessary that each is treated in the correct way. Any floor surface which is porous and has a granular structure needs to be protected. This is done by sealing the surface with a semi-permanent liquid material which penetrates and fills the open pores and dries to give a smooth, hard, and durable finish. This prevents dirt and grease becoming engrained and means that cleaning is simpler and that the floor will retain its attractive appearance for a longer period. Wood, composite, and cork floors must always be sealed; magnesite, flexible P.V.C., concrete, asphalt, and linoleum can be sealed if situated in a heavy traffic area and where maintenance is difficult. These seals penetrate and become part of the floor structure and, although they eventually wear, if they have been applied correctly and are well maintained should last for three or more years.

There are two basic types of polish – one which is solvent-based and the other which has a water-base. In a solvent-based polish the wax is suspended in a white spirit or paraffin; this should not be used on thermoplastic, rubber, vinyl asbestos or asphalt floors as the solvent will soften and eventually crack the surface. Water-based polishes can be used on any type of floor. Many properties can be built into floor polishes: they can clean and polish, be detergent-resistant, be re-buffable or dry-bright. The type used depends on the amount of traffic and dirt to be expected: a dry-bright polish is not suitable in a heavy traffic area; a detergent-resistant emulsion is needed where liquids and light soiling are frequently occurring on the floor; a wash and wax emulsion will loosen dirt which is removed by the applicator and will leave a new layer of polish at the same time.

Floor seals and polishes are discussed fully in Chapter 6 of *Housekeeping Management*.

CARPETS

A good carpet is judged by the density of the tufts in the pile, by the height of the pile in relation to the number of tufts, by the type of fibre used, and by the strength of the carpet backing. A quick method of telling the quality is to bend the carpet back; if the backing is easily seen through the pile the carpet will probably be of medium to poor quality but if it is difficult to see the backing the pile must be thick and closely woven, and should wear well. A good quality carpet may have as many as 125 tufts to the square inch and a poorer quality as few as 50 or less.

To assist the public when buying, the Federation of British Carpet Manufacturers have set up a carpet centre in London which has the largest display of woven carpets in the country. They have also instituted a labelling scheme in which carpets are marked to show their suitability for different areas. Classifications are:

> Light domestic use.
> Light to medium domestic use.
> Medium domestic or light contract use.
> Heavy domestic or medium contract use.
> Luxury domestic or heavy contract use.

Any carpet which carries their label is guaranteed provided it has been used and laid under the conditions which they recommend. It should be noted that not all manufacturers are members of the Federation and that some carpets, often equally good, are not so marked. The scheme does not apply to 'tufted' and other types of carpet.

TYPES OF CARPET AVAILABLE

WOVEN CARPETS

Woven carpets are ones in which the surface pile and the backing are woven together during the manufacture to give very hard wearing properties. Axminsters and Wiltons take their name from the towns in the West country and Wiltshire where each method of weaving was developed, but the name now refers only to the weaving process with production of each type carried out in many parts of the country.

Axminsters

Axminsters are made on two different types of looms, either spool or gripper, and by a third process of manufacture which combines both methods of weaving, spool/gripper; the appearance, however, is indistinguishable whichever is the method of production. Spool and spool/gripper looms can produce carpets with an unlimited number of colours or design; a gripper loom has a normal maximum of eight colours. In all methods, each tuft is individually inserted into the weave so that all the wool is on the surface.

Wiltons

Wiltons are limited to a colour range of five colours. The yarn is woven over thin strips of steel which are the same height as the required depth of the pile, so that a series of loops are left. When the steel strips are withdrawn they cut the loops of the yarn leaving them as tufts securely held by the weft. When different colours are used the yarn is brought to the surface and looped; when it is not needed the yarn is carried in the backing of the carpet in much the same way as the wool is carried in Fair Isle knitting. This gives a Wilton carpet its reputation for 'hidden' strength and resilience.

Cord and Brussels

Cord and Brussels carpets are manufactured in the same way as a Wilton but the steel strips are withdrawn without cutting the loops. A cord is a plain carpet, a Brussels carpet is patterned.

Apart from the number of colours it is possible to introduce into a carpet, an Axminster and a Wilton look similar on the surface but can be told apart by looking at the weft in the backing. In an Axminster, the weft is inserted by a needle, so two rows of thread run side by side. In a Wilton, the weft runs in lines of a single thread.

Wearing properties for both types of weave are very similar given equal quality and conditions of wear. Most manufacturers will produce special designs or colours to match any decorative scheme, provided a reasonable order is given; this at little or no extra cost.

TUFTED CARPETS

Tufted carpets are a relatively recent development but, because manufacture is cheaper and quicker than for woven carpets, they have rapidly taken a large proportion of the market. They are not a woven carpet but have the pile needled into a previously made hessian backing, the tufts being permanently fixed by a latex or plastic backing added to the hessian. Extra strength can be given by adding a further backing of rubber or felt which will prevent the fabric stretching or buckling. These carpets are mainly produced in plain, mottled, or textured designs; patterns are difficult to reproduce with the machinery at its present stage of development.

Tufted carpets have mainly been made from man-made fibres but some are now using a percentage of wool.

ADHESIVELY BONDED CARPETS

Adhesively Bonded Carpets are those in which the pile is stuck to the backing fabric; the pile is usually of short nylon fibres which give a very close, dense, and hard-wearing pile and a velvet appearance. For extra resilience a felt or sponge backing is often added.

A variation of this type of carpet is when the pile is set into a plastic backing and cemented directly to the floor.

CARPET TILES

These were developed in Holland made from synthetic animal or wool fibres which are implanted into a solid base and backed with jute. The surface has a matted effect. These tiles are laid loose and can be taken up and changed round as needed for repair or to give chequered pattern effects.

TYPES OF FIBRE

The ideal fibre should be strong and durable, resistant to stains and fire, and easy to clean. Traditionally wool has always been used for good quality carpets; but because prices fluctuate from year to year there has been increasing use made of the cheaper man-made fibres, either on their own or blended with wool.

WOOL

Wool is still the main fibre used for woven carpets, but it is now often found with a percentage of nylon added, usually in the proportions of 80% wool: 20% nylon. Wool wears well and is warm and comfortable and easy to clean; the nylon gives added wear. Above all, wool is difficult to burn; a cigarette end on a woollen carpet will smoulder and go out leaving only a slight singe mark which can be rubbed off.

Plain or worsted yarn is usually used, the worsteds making the fabric look very smooth and silky.

NYLON

Nylon is tougher than wool, resilient, and very hard wearing. As do other man-made fibres, it soils easily but will also clean easily. Nylon does not burn quickly but will melt when there is extreme heat. A disadvantage of all nylon carpets is that they build up static electricity in dry conditions.

ACRYLICS

These are the acrilan and courtelle fibres which can be bulked to resemble wool. Acrilan is not blended with wool but is used either on its own or with other man-made fibres. Courtelle is blended with wool/nylon/rayon or acrylics.

Acrylics, at present, are flammable.

POLYPROPYLENE

This fibre was developed in the early 1950s and was originally used to replace jute and sisal backing in woven carpets but now it is frequently blended with wool, or used on its own, for carpeting. It is particularly suitable for out-door use as it is non-absorbent and has good resistance to mild chemicals, moulds and fungi.

RAYONS AND MODIFIED RAYON

These are cheaper fibres which are often added to give bulk to the surface pile at a lower price than if an all-wool yarn is used. They are less resilient than the other fibres and crush and soil quickly. Modified rayon blends successfully with wool, nylon, or acrylic.

CARPET BACKING

Traditionally all woven carpets had a backing of hessian, jute, or cotton; now linen, paper, and polyester are also being used. In use some of these backings may stretch. Hessian, jute, and cotton will shrink if they become wet so that with all wet shampooing care must be taken that the water used does not penetrate to the back of the carpet. If a fitted carpet does become wet through flooding, or some of the other causes which can occur, it may be wise to leave it in position to dry rather than to lift it to speed the drying process; otherwise it may not fit quite as well as it did. The problem can be complicated by the state and type of the sub-floor as one would not like a wooden floor to remain wet for any length of time.

Felt, rubber, and sponge backings are now added to many carpets, which may mean that a separate underlay is not necessary. Rubber or sponge backing means that the carpet should not shrink or stretch under any conditions.

UNDERLAYS

Underlays are necessary to prolong the life of the carpet, which they will frequently double. They are also necessary to eliminate any unevenness in the sub-floor and must themselves be laid so that there are no gaps or double thicknesses which will ridge under the carpet and cause wear. The underlay helps to absorb pressure from furniture, gives the carpet a more luxurious feeling underfoot, and provides good heat insulation and sound absorption.

There are two main types of underlay, underfelt and sponge rubber.

UNDERFELT

Underfelt should be used for all body carpet which is joined, as the felt allows the seams to bed down and helps to reduce wear at the joins. A rubber underlay will rub these seams. Felt is usually a mixture of jute and animal hair but in cheaper grades, jute and hair or jute on its own are obtainable, although these crush badly and do not wear so well. The heavier the underfelt the better is the wear; the best protection for the carpet is obtained from one which is at least 13 mm ($\frac{1}{2}$ in.) thick. Underfelt is subject to attack from moths and should be protected by a pesticide.

SPONGE RUBBER

Sponge Rubber is more expensive than felt but is impervious to moth attack and damp and gives a good luxurious base. There is usually a backing of hessian which is placed *upwards* so that the carpet can be pulled over the underlay when it is being laid. Seams are joined by adhesive tape to prevent one edge riding over the other and causing a ridge under the carpet. A compromise between felt and sponge rubber underlays has since been developed; this is a layered combination of felt and rubber.

Where there is a suspended wood sub-floor it is usual to put a layer of felt paper under the underlay; this prevents dirt being drawn up through the floorboards into the carpet by the suction of vacuum cleaners. It is surprising how much dirt can be accumulated under a 'clean' carpet in this way.

An old carpet should not be used as an underlay as there is insufficient resilience left in it and it will rub any seam joins which are not able to bed down properly. The old carpet will be worn in those places where the heaviest tread is found so giving little or no protection to the new carpet.

For stairways, pads of either felt or sponge rubber underlay are used. These are tacked in place 25 mm (1 in.) from the front of the stair riser.

CARPET SIZES

CARPET 'SQUARES'

Carpet 'Squares' can be obtained in many shapes and sizes but are little used for large-scale-work. Their chief advantage is that they may be turned easily to equalize wear, but they are difficult to repair as it is frequently found that wear is limited to one or two areas whilst the rest of the carpet is comparatively unworn. This means that the carpet has either to be cut down and used in a smaller room or else a patch is inserted and, of course, with a carpet square there is often no reserve of carpet for maintenance purposes.

A second very considerable disadvantage is that as the surround to the carpet is of some other floor surface there will be two cleaning processes to carry out.

FITTED CARPETS

Fitted carpets are made from either broadloom or body widths. Traditionally woven carpets are joined by hand-sewing but a faster, stronger method has now been developed. The basis of this is a carpet-tape made from glass fibres impregnated with adhesive and bonded to metal foil. It is joined to the carpet electrically, whilst all latex or sponge-backed carpets are joined by an adhesive tape. A woven carpet has to have any cut edges turned in and bound but this is not necessary for other carpets as when they are cut correctly, there is no chance of the pile fraying.

Broadloom carpet is made in roll-widths of 1 830, 2 285, 2 745, 3 200, 3 660, 4 115 and 4 570 mm or occasionally wider (6 to 18 ft). The width bought must be related to the room size so as to prevent waste in the cutting and fitting.

Body and stair carpet comes in roll-widths of 457, 572, 686 and 914 mm (18 to 36 in.).

When buying fitted carpets it is advisable to buy a reserve length so that worn parts may be replaced. Over the years it will be found that these carpets can be taken up, unsewn, and rejoined to obtain even wear. An extra length is always allowed for stair carpet as, if it is laid in one run, it must be moved 50 to 75 mm (2 to 3 in.) every six months or so to prevent wear marks developing on the tread. The 'lie' of the pile should run downstairs; if it is laid the other way this may cause excessive wear. Stair carpet can also be laid in sections to cover one tread and the riser with the join covered by the stair-nosing.

As with any other pile fabrics, fitted carpets must always be joined in the same 'way' of the material. The carpet is usually cut so that the seams run parallel to the longest side of the room.

CARPET LAYING

Laying of fitted carpets is a skilled job and is best done by the contractors; the underlay must fit and be laid smoothly, and the carpet should be slightly stretched in the laying so that it will not buckle with wear.

The traditional method of laying is to *turn and tack*, nailing the carpet directly to the floor. This can give a wavy line at the edges and result in a torn carpet when it is taken up for maintenance. The tacks can also be unsightly.

The *smooth edge tackless 'gripper'* method was introduced from America in 1955 (*see* Figure 8.1). Wood or metal strips are fitted around the perimeter of the room; the carpet is anchored to them by attaching it to a row of pins which protrude from the wood; the raw edges of the carpet are pushed down tightly between the wood strip and the skirting board. To remove the carpet, a small portion is unhooked and the remainder pulls easily from the gripping pins. A similar method is by *ring and pin*; this is mainly found in the North of England and consists of rings sewn to the under edge of the carpet and attached to pins set in the floor.

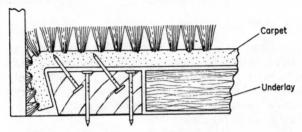

FIGURE 8.1 The 'tackless gripper' method of carpet laying

When carpeting has to be removed regularly, for dancing purposes, *press studs* or *touch and close fasteners* can also be used.

Stair Carpets can be fixed by the tackless gripper method or by stair rods. Stair nosings, of rubber or metal strips, can also be fixed by the gripper method.

CARPET TREATMENT

When new, a woollen carpet should only be brushed lightly or carpet-swept during the first month, to allow the carpet to settle into place and the short loose ends of fibre to mat into the base of the pile to increase the carpet life.

DAILY CLEANING

Vacuum and remove stains as they occur.

PERIODICAL CLEANING

Regular shampooing. If the carpet is laid in a light traffic area this should be done annually, but where there is heavier wear and soiling, shampooing may be needed more frequently to keep the carpet in good condition.

Cleaning may be done *in situ;* this is the quickest method as the room can be back in use as soon as the carpet is dry. Cleaning is more thorough if the carpet is taken up but this involves extra expense and labour and will mean that the room is out of commission for several days.

Carpets are *dry* or *wet* cleaned using either a solvent cleaner or a liquid cleaner. The general procedure for both methods is:

1. Vacuum to remove dirt.
2. Remove stains (*see* notes below).
3. Test for colour fastness by rubbing with a damp cloth. If colour runs, add acetic acid (vinegar) to liquid detergent.
4. Shampoo.
5. Leave to dry.
6. Vacuum to lift pile.

In a *dry cleaner,* the solvent is suspended in an inert powdered carrier; this is applied by a machine which is designed to agitate the pile and to brush the cleaner well in. When the powder feels dry it, and the dirt combined with it, are vacuumed from the carpet.

Instruction notes for carpet cleaning using a liquid detergent cleaner are given in Figure 8.2.

Notes for Instructing Staff

HOW TO SHAMPOO A FITTED CARPET

Equipment required: A vaccum cleaner, a carpet shampooing/ scrubbing machine, a wet suction cleaner. A hand scrubbing brush, clean cloths. Stain remover, an approved carpet detergent, acetic acid.

What to do	*Main points to mention*
Assemble equipment	
Remove all furniture to give a clear working area	Store or place tidily so as not to inconvenience guests or other staff
Vacuum clean carpet	To remove as much dirt and grit as possible and to raise the pile. Pay particular attention to corners and edges
Treat for stains	Type of stain remover to use
Test for colour fastness	Use a damp cloth; if colour will run, add acetic acid to detergent solution (1:80)
With hand scrubber and detergent solution, scrub the perimeter of the carpet 230 to 300 mm (9 to 12 in.) in from edge	This ensures all the carpet is cleaned

What to do	Points to mention
Machine scrub the remainder of carpet working in strips across floor	Control detergent release on machine so that carpet does not become too wet
Leave carpet to dry	Ensure that during this time, no furniture is replaced or the carpet trodden on
When dry, vacuum well to raise the pile	Replace furniture only when completely dry; otherwise indentation marks or rust marks are made

Discuss the advantages of working in pairs as a team for this and other types of cleaning

FIGURE 8.2

As an interim measure, chamois leather or net cloth which has been wrung out in detergent and water and rubbed firmly over the carpet will brighten it and remove some of the surface dirt.

STAIN REMOVAL

All marks and stains should be removed as soon as possible before they become engrained and permanent.

Most *new* stains can be partly or wholly removed by one of the following methods, or a combination of both.

1. Dry cleaning

Using a cleaning solvent such as carbon tetrachloride, benzol, or a proprietary make; the stain is rubbed gently with a soft cloth, working from the outside towards the centre. This prevents a 'tide-mark' effect. The cloth is changed as needed. (A dry cleaning solvent should not come in contact with a rubber or plastic backing to the carpet.)

2. Wet cleaning

Using either plain water or a liquid detergent, the stain is rubbed gently as before whilst keeping the carpet as dry as possible in the process. The stain is rubbed and blotted off until there is no further improvement.

Oils, fats, grease, tar, and paint are treated by method 1. Beers, wines, spirits, fresh ink, and shoe polish (after it has been scraped off) by method 2.

Coffee, tea, milk, cocoa, and soft drinks are treated by method 2 followed by method 1.

Rust by method 2 and then the area rinsed with a warm strong solution of oxalic acid. Rinse well with clear water and mop dry.

Salt, liquids and urine are mopped up, then treated by method 2 but with the addition of 1 part white vinegar to each 10 parts of detergent solution; salt will affect the colour fastness, and the vinegar should prevent the colour running.

Chewing Gum is softened by cleaning solvent and scraped off using a blunt knife. In stubborn cases dry ice is very effective. Aerosols are also available. These are filled with a chemical which reduces the temperature to below freezing point. This makes the chewing gum easily removable with a knife, or it can be broken up and removed by a vacuum cleaner as a hard dry dust.

To prevent staining, a special *silicone* finish can be applied to carpets, rugs, and upholstery. This is sprayed on to a well-cleaned carpet; the silicone forms an invisible shield around each fibre which makes it dirt, oil, and water repellent, and increases the fire resistant properties. A silicone protection can be applied to both wool and man-made fibres and it makes dirt removal much easier. The fabric can still be wet-cleaned, but dry cleaning solvents remove the silicone protection .

CARPET PROBLEMS

FADING AND COLOUR FASTNESS

Even the best quality dyes can fade if a carpet is exposed to strong sunlight and, where there are these conditions, the carpet should be protected by drawn curtains or sun-blinds. In a good quality thick carpet the signs of fading can be removed by shearing the carpet or by careful shaving with a razor to remove the top surface from the fibres. This is also a good method of removing discoloration or singe marks which cannot be removed in any other way.

In a poor quality carpet the colour may run from one pattern into another if the pile has been allowed to remain wet or damp.

SHADING

This is mainly noticeable in plain or 'velvet' textured carpets and is caused by slight differences in the 'lie' of the pile. This difference is very noticeable if strip carpet has been joined with the strips running in opposite directions; to avoid this, when cut the carpet should be marked on the back with arrow directions so that there can be no mistake.

SHOOTING

A tuft shooting or standing out above the rest of the pile should be cut back level and not pulled out. In cord carpets a loop may be caught and pulled up; this should be eased back by using a knitting needle or hook to pull the adjacent loops back to the correct height.

MOTHS AND CARPET BEETLES

These only attack wool by eating the keratin in the fibres; man-made fibres are not affected. All wool or wool mixture carpets should be moth-proofed during manufacture but this proofing may have to be renewed after dry or wet shampooing and should be done by specialists. Moth and carpet beetle pesticides are available but will usually not penetrate to the roots of the tufts where the larvae are to be found and where they are often out of reach of normal cleaning methods (*see* Figure 8.3).

FIGURE 8.3   Carpet beetle and moth larvae

MILDEW

If the carpet becomes wet through water seeping from leaking radiators or pipes, spilt liquids, or insufficient drying after wet cleaning, mildew can develop and, if left, will eventually rot the carpet.

CARPET AND FLOOR PROTECTION

1. Ensure that carpets and floor are not torn or scraped by furniture being dragged over them. Have castors fitted which are metal or plastic and which will not leave rust marks on the floor.
2. Use druggets (of thick linen or canvas) to cover and protect the floor or carpet in bad weather or when there is any re-decoration or movement of stores or equipment.
3. Prevent dirt being brought into the building by using adequate mats or grilles at all entrances. The best type seem to be the newer rubber grilles which can be either free-standing or sunk into a 25 mm (1 in.) well. These provide a surface that removes dirt from the soles of footwear by a flicking action of the rubber sections; the dirt is retained in the spaces between the sections and can only

be removed by suction cleaner. These grilles can be made to any size but should be wide enough for both feet to tread on whilst entering. These cavity mats are a legal requirement for hospitals in all Scandinavian countries.

Fibre mats retain a considerable amount of dirt *but* are heavy, retain moisture, are difficult to dry, and are extremely difficult to clean adequately either by shaking outside or by using a suction cleaner.

Impregnated rugs collect dirt quite effectively but are easily kicked out of place.

APPENDIX

* Hotels and inns generally of small scale with acceptable facilities and furnishings. All bedrooms with hot and cold water; adequate bath and lavatory arrangements. Meals are provided for residents but their availability to non-residents may be limited.
** Hotels offering a higher standard of accommodation and some private bathrooms/showers. A wider choice of food is provided but the availability of meals to non-residents may be limited.
*** Well appointed hotels with more spacious accommodation with a large number of bedrooms with private bathrooms/showers. Fuller meal facilities are provided but for luncheon and at weekends service to non-residents may be restricted.
**** Exceptionally well-appointed hotels offering a high standard of comfort and service with the majority of bedrooms providing private bathrooms/showers.
***** Luxury hotels offering the highest international standards.
Ap Hotels which conform to most star classification requirements and are worthy of recommendation.
♣♣ The symbol used to denote an AA Country House Hotel where a relaxed informal atmosphere and personal welcome prevail. However, some of the facilities may differ from those found in urban hotels of the same classification. These hotels are often secluded but not always rurally situated.
White Stars The method used to indicate establishments high in amenities but with deliberately limited personalized services designed and operated to cater predominantly for the short stay guest. Under this heading will be found some motels and motor hotels with bedroom facilities mainly on a self service basis. It is emphasized that white stars are an indication of a type of hotel.

The principal requirements for the accommodation services, so that a common standard is achieved throughout the country, are listed below. Whatever its type and classification every Appointed hotel must provide:

1. A reasonable standard of exterior decoration.

2. A high standard of cleanliness, hygiene, and furnishing.
3. Prompt and courteous service.
4. Adequately lighted and heated public rooms.
5. An indication of how to obtain emergency assistance at night.
6. Lighting of bedroom corridors during the hours of darkness.
7. In all bedrooms or their private bathrooms these items:
   (*a*) Wash-basin with hot and cold running water, soap, towel, and mirror over the wash-basin. Glass tumbler for each person.
   (*b*) Single beds should be at least 200 cm (6 ft 6 in.) long and 100 cm (3 ft 3 in.) wide; double beds should be 200 cm (6 ft 6 in.) long and 150 cm (5 ft) wide. Mattresses should be modern.
   (*c*) Thick curtains, blinds, or shutters with drapes.
   (*d*) Bedside or bedhead table, cabinet, or shelf.
   (*e*) Dressing table or vanitory unit.
   (*f*) A chair per person.
   (*g*) Wardrobe or other provision for hanging clothes.
   (*h*) Drawers or shelves.
   (*i*) Carpet, or rug for each bed.
   (*j*) Means of securing the door from inside and outside.
   (*k*) Hot water bottle on request.
8. Bathrooms furnished with stool, chair or lidded W.C., towel rail, bath mat, receptacle for soap, and hook for clothes.

REFERENCES

HMSO Publications

Student Residence; Building Bulletin 37 – University Building Notes (Department of Education and Science).

Training College Hostels; Building Bulletin 15 (Ministry of Education).

Space in the Home (metric edition); Design Bulletin 6 (Ministry of Housing and Local Government).

Residential Accommodation for Staff; Hospital Building Note 24 (Ministry of Health).

Flatlets for Old People.

More Flatlets for Old People (Ministry of Housing and Local Government).

Lighting in Offices, Shops and Railway Premises (Department of Employment and Productivity).

A Short History of Lighting; The Science Museum (Ministry of Education).

Building Research Station

Hostel User Study, by Phyllis Allen (Current Papers).
Principles of Sun Control, by P. Petherbridge (Current Papers).
Sound Insulation of Windows, by R. M. Wooley (Design Paper 64).
U-values in the 1970 guide, by A. G. Loudon (Current Papers).
Trial of plastic pipes for hot water services, by J. R. Crowder and
A. Rixon (Current Papers).
The Maintenance and Running Costs of School Building, by M. A.
Clapp and B. D. Cullen (Current Papers).

Reports to the Council of Industrial Design

On Carpets and Bathrooms.

King Edward's Hospital Fund for London

Floor Maintenance in Hospital Wards; a progress report by F. E.
Burnham.

AJ Metric Handbook (The Architectural Press).
Packaged Air Conditioning; a guide prepared by the Electricity
Council.
Timber Preservation (British Wood Preserving Association, Timber
Research and Development Association).
General publications from the Infestation Control Division of the
Ministry of Agriculture, Fisheries, and Food.
Electricity and Home Appliances (Electrical Association for
Women).
Lighting for Hotels and Restaurants (The Electricity Council).
The Theory and Practice of Public Health, by W. Hobson (Oxford
University Press).
Housekeeping Manual for Health Care Facilities (American Hospital
Association, Chicago).

INDEX